Instructor's Guide & Answer Key for use with the book DRAFTING

by Walter C. Brown

Published by

THE GOODHEART-WILLCOX CO., INC.

Instructor's Guide and Answer Key for use with

DRAFTING

by Walter C. Brown

Drafting is a text in Goodheart-Willcox's Build-A-Course GENERAL SHOP SERIES. It is designed as a student oriented text which enables the student to explore the broad field of drafting, and at the same time develop the necessary skills needed in reading shop drawings and sketches. The text is organized so it may be used as a block unit in a general shop course in combination with other texts in this Series. Sufficient content is also included to meet the needs of a semester course in beginning drafting.

The basic skills and informational content are discussed in words which are easily understood by the student. The many illustrations further clarify the written material and enhance the student's interest.

The use of this student oriented text allows the instructor more time for demonstrations, class discussions, individual instruction, and student evaluation.

SEQUENCE OF UNITS

It is recommended that the first six units be completed before permitting the student to progress to other units. Once Unit 2 has been completed, the student should use his sketching ability to "block out" the problems in succeeding units. This will help the student to develop the habit of analyzing his problem before he makes an instrument drawing.

Units 7, through 13, may be presented in most any sequence which meets the instructional need.

The skills of blueprint reading will be fairly well developed in Units 1 through 13. However, Unit 14 provides information on various kinds of prints, and gives the student an opportunity to apply some of his drafting skills and knowledge to the reading of prints.

DRAFTING ACTIVITIES

Specific assignments are made to the student in each unit under the heading "Drafting Activity." These activities are correlated with the textual materials and presented at the optimum time for learning.

All students should complete the basic drafting activities in each unit. Individual differences between students may be provided for in the drafting activities near the end of each unit. The creative instructor will also make additional assignments to meet particular instructional needs.

INSTRUCTIONAL AIDS IN DRAFTING

The following aids are only suggestive of the many which are available to drafting instructors. Such aids will do much to add interest and enthusiasm for your students.

Films - Check the film catalogs in your area for films on:

1. Industrial uses of drafting
2. Drawing and sketching techniques
3. Reproduction processes in drafting
4. Occupational opportunities in drafting
5. Construction work

Models - These may be collected, purchased, or constructed for class use.

1. Wooden or plastic models of objects to be used with a projection box
2. Actual objects from the machine shop or woodworking industry
3. Sheet metal elbows, T's, etc. (These may be paper or actual sheet metal pieces)
4. Scale model of house construction
5. Large size model of draftsman's flat or triangular scale

Displays - Some items may be secured from industry and school supply firms at little or no cost.

1. Photos of drawing instruments, equipment, and supplies
2. Drawings and prints from industry
3. Student "drawing of the week"
4. Industrial products showing need for drafting
5. Photos of industrial drafting rooms

Field Trips - These are sometimes difficult to schedule but they are one of the best means of creating interest and presenting occupational information.

1. Industrial drafting rooms to observe draftsmen at work, industrial practices in drafting, types of drawings being used, equipment used, and print reproduction processes
2. Drafting rooms at state highway and county surveyor's offices
3. Residential and commercial building construction jobs
4. Sheet metal shop to observe uses of sheet metal layouts
5. Print reproduction plants

DRAFTING

Answer Key

UNIT 1

Fig. 1-7 (page 10) Scale-Reading Problem

a, b, c, are given	i - 1/2
d - 3 5/8	j - 1/8
e - 4 7/8	k - 5/8
f - 2 1/8	l - 3/8
g - 1 1/4	m - 7/16
h - 1 1/2	n - 1/16

Fig. 1-8 (page 10) C-Clamp Measurement Problem

a - 5 1/8, b - 1/2, c - 3/8, d - 3 3/8, e - 7/8, f - 1/2, g - 1, h - 2 7/8

***Note to Instructor:** Answers given here to C-clamp measuring problem should be verified. Uneven stretching of paper while printing prevents our answers from being 100% accurate for all copies of the book.*

QUIZ (page 23)

1. Means of communicating an idea; it is a graphic language of lines, symbols, sizes, and space relationships.
2. Changes in units of measurement and notes.
3. Student response.
4. Keep hands clean, remove erasure dust, sharpen pencil away from drawing, draw all lines lightly at first.
5. To prevent gouging of the paper.
6. Ink erasers scratch the surface of drawing paper.
7. This will discolor the scale and make it difficult to read.
8. A smooth surface and a straight working edge.
9. 1 1/4 in.
10. Border line.

UNIT 2

QUIZ (page 29)

1. Quick methods of drawing an object; helpful in planning an instrument drawing.
2. Pencil, erasers, and paper.
3. By eying the point where line is to end.
4. Proper relation of things or parts. Essential to good sketches.
5. Student response.
6. See page 29. Should be used after the freehand sketching technique is learned to improve quality and speed in sketching.

UNIT 3

QUIZ (page 39)

1. Supplies information needed in constructing or servicing an object.
2. Perpendicular or right-angle projection.
3. One. All necessary details are shown in one view.
4. Student response.
5. Give priority to the front view, position for best shape description, normal resting position, least hidden lines, and best arrangement on plate.
6. To show edges, surfaces, and corners which are not visible in a particular view.
7. Chief draftsman, designer, detailer, checker, and tracer. Duties on page 37.
8. Neatness, accuracy, normal vision, and considerable technical knowledge. Some industries require previous training in drafting.

9. Works with ideas and problems related to the transformation of materials into products useful to man. Should have high aptitude and ability in English, math, science, and drafting. Four to five years of college training.
10. Designs buildings with concern for construction, appearance, and function. Four to five years of college.
11. Teaches junior and senior high students in one or more areas such as drafting. Work is pleasant, creative, and provides considerable freedom. Four to five years of college are required.

UNIT 4

QUIZ (page 46)

1. Can be lettered more readily and is easier to read.
2. Vertical and inclined.
3. Capitals for title block information and notes. Capitals and lower case used sometimes for notes.
4. Capitals 1/8 in. Lower case is 2/3 height of capital. Numerals same as capitals and fractions are twice the height of whole numbers.
5. One letter space between words; two letter spaces between sentences.
6. For all lettering. So light they need not be erased.
7. Place a sheet of paper or cloth under your hand and arm.
8. Kind of material, finish, and quantity.
9. Approximately 1/8 in. long and 1/3 as wide.
10. Procedures in drafting which makes use of "shortcuts" and still maintains accuracy. Examples: dots for arrowheads, elimination of views for use of a shop note, freehand sketches in place of instrument drawings, and the use of abbreviations and symbols on drawings.

UNIT 5

QUIZ (page 51)

1. From the view in which the inclined surface appears as a line. Necessary to get true length.
2. Usually, not more than two.
3. When you want to show the true size and shape of an inclined surface.
4. An auxiliary view projected from the right side view.
5. To show more clearly the shape and operation of complex objects.
6. In the full section, the imaginary cutting plane pass all the way through the object. Only halfway through the object in a half section.
7. When the shape and position of the object is such that 45 deg. lines would be parallel or perpendicular (or nearly so) to a prominent visible line bounding the sectional area.
8. When the section lines are not being used to indicate type of material.

UNIT 6

Note to Instructor: Answers given here to measuring problems 6-3, 6-6, 6-8, and 6-10, should be verified. Uneven stretching of paper while printing prevents our answers from being 100% accurate for all copies of the book.

Fig. 6-3 (page 54) Measuring problem
Half-size Scale - a-10 in., b-8 1/2 in., c-7 3/4 in., d-5 1/4 in.

Fig. 6-6 (page 55) Measuring problem
Quarter-size scale -a=1' - 10", b=1' - 7 1/2", c=1' - 1 3/4", d=11 1/4"

Fig. 6-8 (page 55) Measuring problem
Scale 1 1/2" = 1", 3/4 in., 3/4 in., 3/4 in., 1/8 in.

Fig. 6-10 (page 56) Measuring problem
Scales vary - a=24'-4", b=14'-6", c=7'-3", d=9'-11",e=37'-0"

QUIZ (page 58)

1. Drawing of an object smaller or larger than its actual size.
2. Architect's scale--inches or fractions of an inch represent feet. Civil engineer's scale--divided into decimal parts of an inch. Mechanical engineer's scale--major end units represent 1 inch rather than a foot.
3. When it is necessary to get it on a reasonable size sheet of paper.
4. In order to show details more clearly.
5. Student response.

UNIT 7

QUIZ (page 67)

1. Isometric and oblique.
2. For better illustration of objects as they appear when you look at them.
3. Isometric--30 deg. Oblique--remain horizontal in front view, usually 45 deg. in inclined view, but can be 30 deg. or 60 deg.
4. In the cabinet oblique, the depth is sometimes foreshortened to one-half of its true length.
5. Dimension lines are parallel to the axes and extension lines are projected in line with the surface or distance dimensioned. Dimension figures are also in line with the surface or distance dimensioned.

UNIT 8

QUIZ (page 71)

1. The series circuit provides a single continuous path in which the current flows. In the parallel circuit, the current has two or more paths to follow.
2. a. Wiring diagrams are pictorial drawings of electrical assembles.
   b. Schematic diagrams make use of electrical symbols instead of pictorial representation of parts. They do not show the location of parts or wiring connections.
   c. Block diagrams are simplified drawings of electrical sections.
3. a. Wiring diagrams show the arrangment of parts and how they are connected together.
   b. Schematic diagrams show the functional relationship of electrical parts to each other and to the entire circuit.
   c. Block diagrams show the relationship of the various sections of an electrical device.
4. Block diagrams.
5. Wiring diagrams.
6. Location of switches, ceiling outlets, and wall outlets. Lines should be drawn from switches to outlets they control.
7. No particular size. They should be drawn correctly, in proportion and about the weight of visible lines.

UNIT 9

QUIZ (page 75)

1. Student response.
2. Figures having many sides, especially figures with more than four sides.

3. Accuracy is essential to the construction of geometric forms.
4. Student response.

UNIT 10

QUIZ (page 81)

1. Because the patterns are laid out or "stretched" out in the flat.
2. Sheet metal, air conditioning, heating, welding, and pipefitting.
3. They are used to develop actual sheet metal parts.
4. By stepping off the circumference with the dividers. Yes, mathematically figuring the circumference.

UNIT 11

Drafting Activity (page 86)

1. 60' -0"x26' -6"
2. 2' -6"
3. LR 20' -5" x 14' -7"; Front BR 13' -2" x 11' -1"; Back Corner BR 9' -11" x 11' -5"; Center Back BR 10' -0" x 10' -5" (Note: some closet walls are only 4" thick)
4. 7' -11"
5. BR Hall 3' -0"; Front Hall 5' -9"; Stairwell 3' -0".
6. Convenience outlets 28; Ceiling outlets 15; Wall outlets 5; single-pole switches 11; three-way switches 5.

QUIZ (page 87-88)

1. (a) Design of the exterior and interior, (b) preparation of drawings, (c) written specifications.
2. Specifications describe those things such as quality of materials, kinds of finish, and types of electrical fixtures which cannot be drawn on the plans.
3. Gable, gambrel, hips, and shed.
4. Traditional and contemporary. Student response on styles.
5. Protected or recessed entrance, entrance hall, kitchen with ample cabinet space and work areas, family or recreation room, adequate closet space, storage space for tools and yard equipment.
6. Floor plan, elevations, detail drawings, perspective, and renderings.
7. See Fig. 11-9, page 87

UNIT 12

QUIZ (page 92)

1. They make factual information more understandable.
2. Bar, line, and pie.
3. Student response.
4. Use the horizontal bar when the number of items to be shown is large.
5. The number of bars, the space between bars, and the height or scale of the graph.
6. The line graph is often the most effective.
7. The pie or circle graph.
8. Organizational chart--to show clearly the relationship of personnel within an organization. Flow chart--to show the route or flow of a certain product or process.

UNIT 13

QUIZ (page 97)

1. Draftsmen draw the maps from data supplied by civil engineers, surveyors, and aerial photographers.

2. The land's surface including hills, valleys, streams, lakes, and trees.
3. Shows the earth's physical features, both natural and man made. It is used in geography texts and usually represents large areas.
4. They are used to show variations in land elevation and are needed in initial planning of highway, building, and other construction projects. They usually show only the contour lines of elevations.
5. The map of a small piece of ground used to show boundary lines and building location.
6. As the name suggests, they present a pictorial view, or birdseye-view, of the area rather than a top view. These maps are used to show principal points of interest and to give directions.

UNIT 14

Blueprint Reading Activity (page 100)

1. Four
2. 19/32 in.
3. 7/8 in.; 1/2 in. No. 20 National Fine Thread, class 3 fit.
4. Tool steel; 3/4 in. diameter and at least 7 1/4 in. long.
5. 1/2 in.
6. 5/16 in.
7. .310 in.; 7/16 in.
8. 20 ga. music wire; 5/16 in.
9. Flat section of body and plunger to 1/2 in. from end.
10. Student response.

Blueprint Reading Activity (page 101)

1. Width 18 in.; length 42 in.; height 14 in.
2. Length 12 3/4 in.; large dia. 1 5/8 in.; small dia. 3/4 in.
3. By a mounting plate and hanger bolt.
4. Centered at 6 1/2 in. from end of top and 2 1/4 in. from edge parallel to a diagonal line across the corners of the top.
5. 5/8 in. or 3/4 in. plywood.
6. Side pieces are 3/4 in. by 1 3/4 in. by 42 in. End pieces are 3/4 in. by 1 3/4 in. by 18 in.
7. Four mounting plates, four hanger bolts, and four metal ferrules--a total of 12 pieces.
8. Student response.

QUIZ (page 102)

1. Blueprints and positive prints. The blueprint has white lines on a dark blue background and the positive prints have dark lines on a light background.
2. Tracings. They are prepared on their transparent paper or cloth by tracing a drawing. The original drawing may also be made directly on tracing paper.
3. The tracing is placed over the light-sensitized paper and exposed to the sun or the strong light of a print making machine.
4. Blueprints--the chemical on the coated paper receiving the light becomes insoluable and when washed in water turns blue. The chemical beneath the lines is soluable and washes away leaving the white paper showing. Positive prints--the light causes the chemically-coated paper to fade. When exposed to the developer solution, the area affected by the light comes out white and the unexposed chemical turns a dark color.
5. <u>Blueprints</u>--Advantages - less expensive, quite durable, does not fade. Disadvantages--difficult to make changes or notes on dark background.
   <u>Positive prints</u>--Advantages - do not shrink in developing process, notes or changes can be added easily. Disadvantages--fade in strong light.

Goodheart-Willcox's BUILD-A-COURSE Series

DRAFTING

by

WALTER C. BROWN

Professor of Industrial Education

Arizona State University, Tempe

Consulting Editor, Build-A-Course Series

Books in Build-A-Course Series

Woodworking—Wagner

Drafting—Brown

Electricity—Gerrish

Electronics—Gerrish

Metalworking—Boyd

Art Metals—Siegner

Graphics Arts—Kagy

Power Mechanics—Atteberry

Leathercraft—Zimmerman

Ceramics—Brennan

Plastics—Cope

(Other books in work)

South Holland, Ill.

THE GOODHEART-WILLCOX CO., Inc.

Publishers

Printed in the United States of America

Library of Congress Catalog
Card Number: 64-14096

122-L

INTRODUCTION

This book is one of a series planned specifically for Industrial Arts General Shop courses. It is designed to provide a broad experience in drafting and to enable one to develop the necessary skills to use drafting effectively.

The book progresses systematically through the skills and informational content basic to an understanding of drafting. In addition to a broad coverage of industrial activities, units are included on graphs, charts, and maps.

It is the author's belief, confirmed by many other Industrial Arts instructors, that students want to work with the tools and materials of industry when they come to the shop or drafting room. To make the most of this interest factor, the author has introduced in Unit 1, instrument usage and drafting fundamentals.

Freehand sketching is then presented in the second unit to acquaint the student with this important phase of drafting. This will enable him to make use of sketching along with instrument drafting in the remaining units.

It is the author's hope that this book will provide students with valuable consumer knowledge, and that it will make drafting a meaningful experience for them in both their avocational and vocational activities.

Walter C. Brown

All manufactured products were first created on the drawing board. (Boeing Co.)

CONTENTS

INTRODUCTION TO DRAFTING

1. **What is drafting?**
2. **How can we use drafting, now and later?**
3. **What are some of the basic skills in the field of drafting?**

A CHAT WITH YOUR INSTRUCTOR

You are about to begin an interesting and fascinating study of another language. Had you thought of drafting in this way? In a very real sense, this is true. It is a means of communication that is often referred to as the "language of industry." It is not a "spoken" language; it is a "graphic" language of:

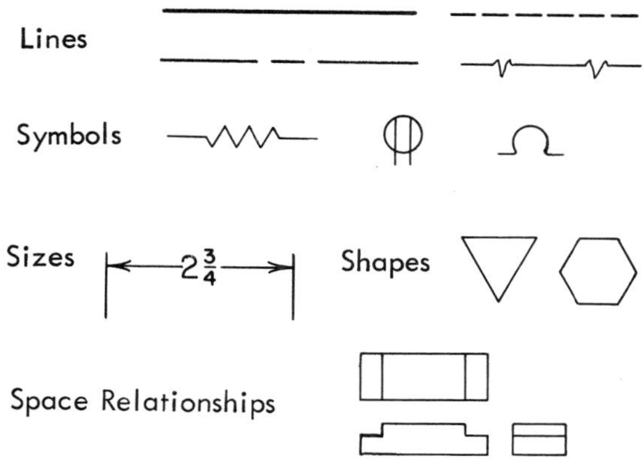

With changes in the units of measurements and the notes, it can be understood equally well by a draftsman in Buenos Aires, Paris, or Moscow. Drafting is the language every technical person uses to communicate his ideas clearly and concisely to others. It is a process of thinking, planning, and setting thoughts down on paper in graphic form. These forms appear as one of several kinds of drawings: multiview, pictorial, pattern, charts, maps, or schematics.

Almost before you realize it, you will be using this language.

IMPORTANCE OF DRAFTING

Most manufactured products and all major buildings were first created on a drawing board. Before your school building could be constructed, or the machines in your school shop manufactured, many hours were spent in preparing detailed drawings. Industry, as we know it today, could not exist without a quick and economical means of communicating its dreams into reality.

Have you ever stopped to think that before your family car was built it was first a drawing--not just the car as we see it, but every bolt, pin, shaft, cylinder, and detail in it. Imagine the number of hours spent preparing the drawings for a jet aircraft. Yes, draftsmen had to draw every detail before it could be built, and do you know that not one of those draftsmen was born with a knowledge of drawing!

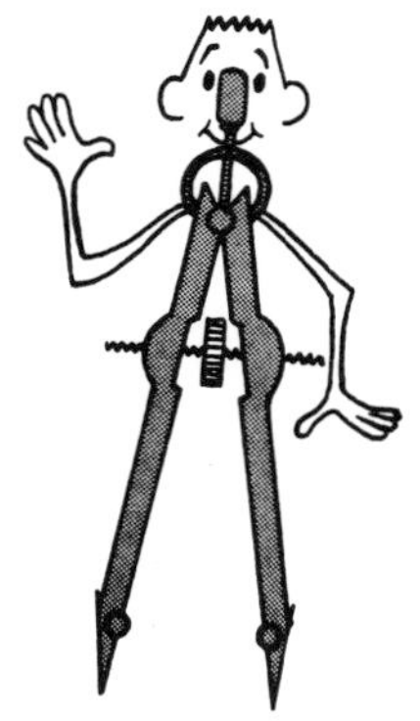

"Hi! I'm Drafty. I'll be around from time to time with pointers and helpful suggestions."

WHO USES DRAFTING?

A thorough knowledge of drafting is es-

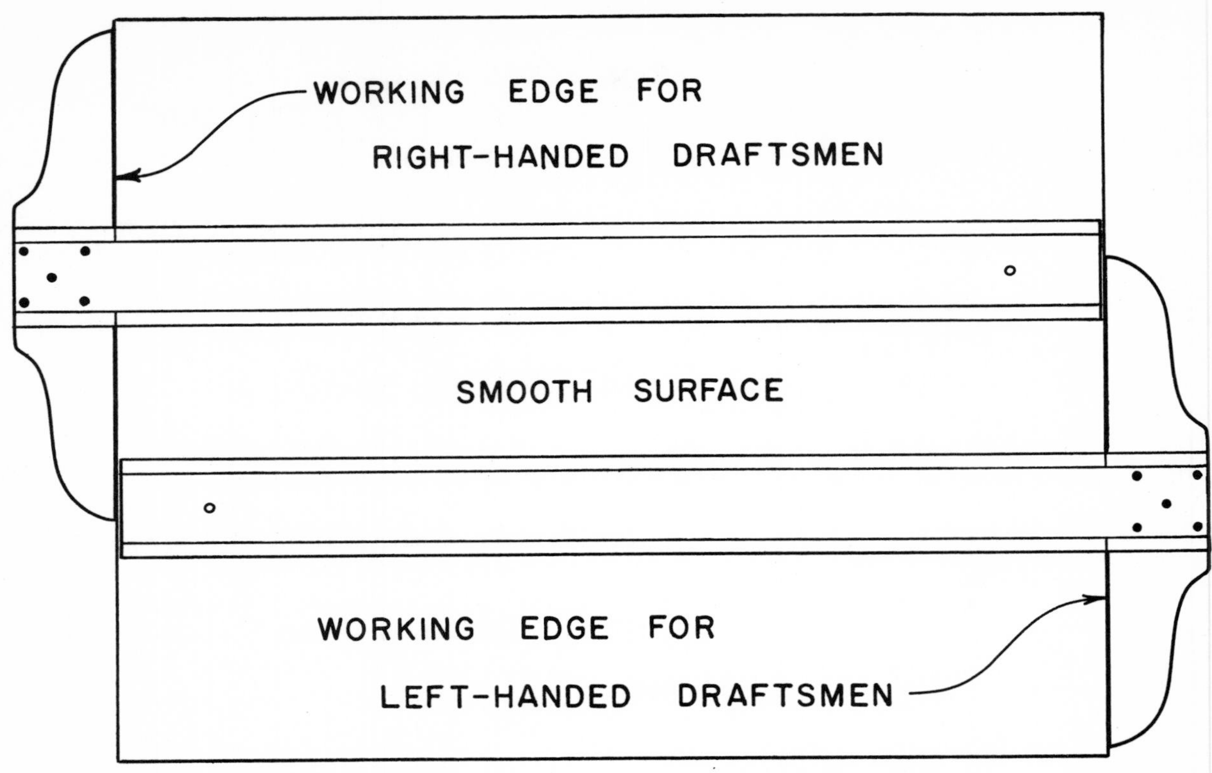

Fig. 1-1. Drawing board showing location of T-square.

sential to the skilled worker, the technician, and the engineer. It is also of value to the hobbyist and homemaker as he or she undertakes jobs in the home workshop and around the house.

Some of your classmates, perhaps even yourself, may become full-time technical workers in the field of drafting. Many of you will use your knowledge of drafting indirectly in your work. All of you will use products of industry, and a knowledge of drafting will be to your advantage.

Everything you do in the industrial arts shop will depend in part upon your ability to sketch, draw, and read drawings. You can also put your knowledge of drafting to work in your other school subjects when you have jobs to do, such as drawing a chart or a graph.

SELECTION AND CARE OF DRAWING BOARDS

There are at least two requirements of a good drawing board: a smooth surface and a straight working edge. See Fig. 1-1. In making drawing boards, both white pine and basswood are used extensively, because their uniform grain textures provide a smooth drawing surface. Since the edge of a drawing board is the reference line for all drawings, it is essential that it be a straight edge. Drawing boards are made in a variety of sizes; the 16 x 22 in. or the 18 x 24 in. size will be suitable for most work.

A skilled craftsman, technician, or engineer is known in part by the care he gives his tools and equipment. You should avoid marring the surface of your drawing board with pencil marks. Use drafting tape, when available, instead of thumb tacks, for fastening drawing paper on the board.

DRAWING PAPERS

Drawing papers are available in a number of colors and sizes. The draftsman selects the color and size most suited to his purpose. Colors ordinarily used are cream, buff, light green, and

white. Common sizes of drawing papers are:

8-1/2 x 11 in.
11 x 17 in.
17 x 22 in.

For your use in this course, 8-1/2 x 11 in. paper should be used. It can be assembled in your notebook after your drawing has been checked. Your instructor will indicate the color of paper you should use.

THE T-SQUARE

The T-square consists of a head and a blade, made of hardwood, which are fastened together securely. Some T-squares have blades with plastic edges which permit a better view of the work. Fig. 1-2.

Fig. 1-2. T-square is held firmly against working edge of drawing board.

The T-square is held firmly against the working edge of the drawing board, Fig. 1-2. It is used for squaring the paper on the board before fastening, for drawing horizontal lines, and as a straight edge for the triangles.

DRAWING PENCILS

Did you know that a draftsman does not buy just any pencil? He selects pencils according to the grade (hardness) of the leads and sharpens them in a manner that will help him produce quality work. There are eighteen grades of pencils from which to select; however, few draftsmen will use this many. Shown in Fig. 1-3 are the grades of drawing pencils and their suggested uses.

For your work in beginning drafting, you will need a 2H pencil for general work. You may later want to get a 4H pencil for layout work and an F or HB pencil for lettering and sketching.

SHARPENING THE DRAWING PENCIL

Drawing pencils may be sharpened with a sharp knife or a pencil sharpener, but the latter wastes more of the lead unless it is a special drafting pencil sharpener. In the event your school does not have a drafting pencil sharpener, you will most likely be using a knife to sharpen your pencil. This method is discussed here.

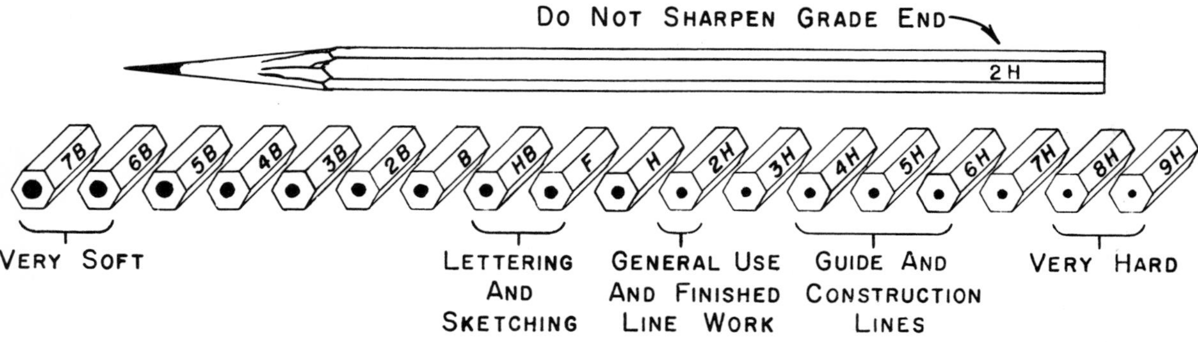

Fig. 1-3. Drawing pencil grades.

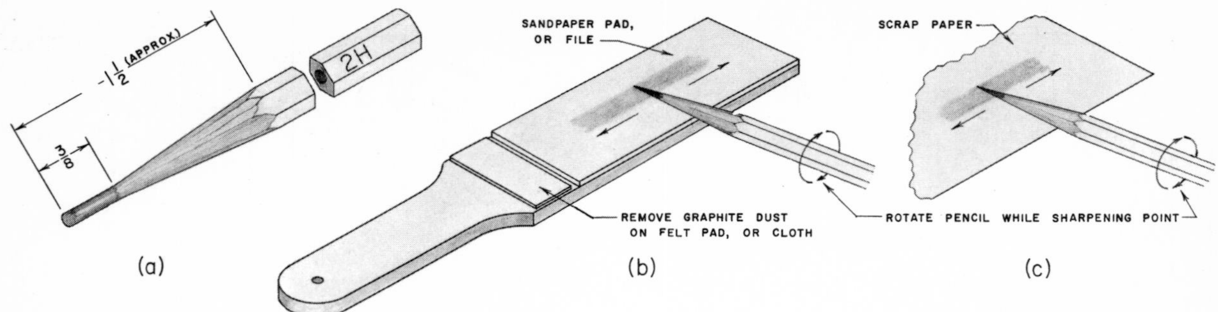

Fig. 1-4. Steps in sharpening a drawing pencil.

Sharpen the pencil on the end opposite the grade marking. Remove enough wood to expose approximately 3/8 in. of lead, Fig. 1-4a. After the lead has been exposed, shape the lead to a long conical point using a sandpaper pad or file, Fig. 1-4b. For final shaping, the point should be finished on a piece of scrap paper, Fig. 1-4c. Remove all excess graphite dust from the pencil point by wiping it on a felt pad or soft cloth.

DRAFTING ACTIVITY

Sharpen your 2H drawing pencil.

DRAFTY SAYS:

"Never sharpen your pencil over the drawing board or instruments. Care should also be taken to keep your hands clean in order to produce clean and neat drawings."

MEASURING WITH THE FULL-SIZE SCALE

The word "scale" in drafting refers both to the instrument used, Fig. 1-5, and to the size an object is drawn, such as, "full-size" or "1/4 scale."

You will find that, next to the pencil, the scale (ruler to grade school students) is one of the most frequently used tools. Accuracy in measuring is very important, for the work of the draftsman affects the work of many others concerned with the object being drawn.

In your beginning plates (drawings), all measurements should be made full-size. With later plates, you will get experience using the 1/2 scale, 1/4 scale, and others familiar to draftsmen.

Fig. 1-5. A triangular and a flat scale used in drafting. (Keuffel & Esser Co.)

The best way to learn the proper measuring techniques and to develop accuracy is with a full-size scale. Perhaps you have already had experience with this scale; if so, the following will refresh your memory.

Refer to Fig. 1-6. This is the full size

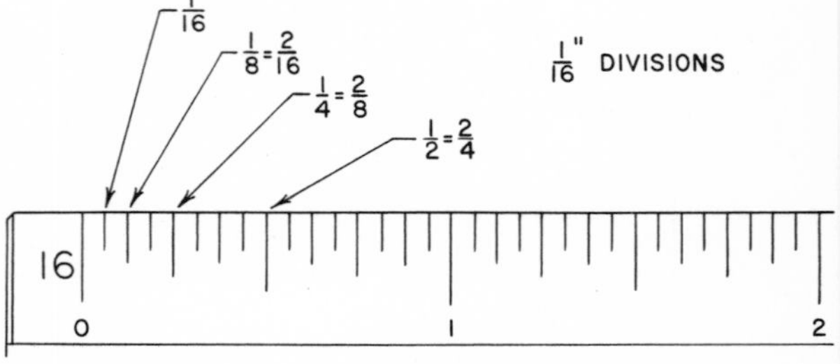

Fig. 1-6. Architect's scale.

scale on the architect's scale. You will note that the dimensions are the same as

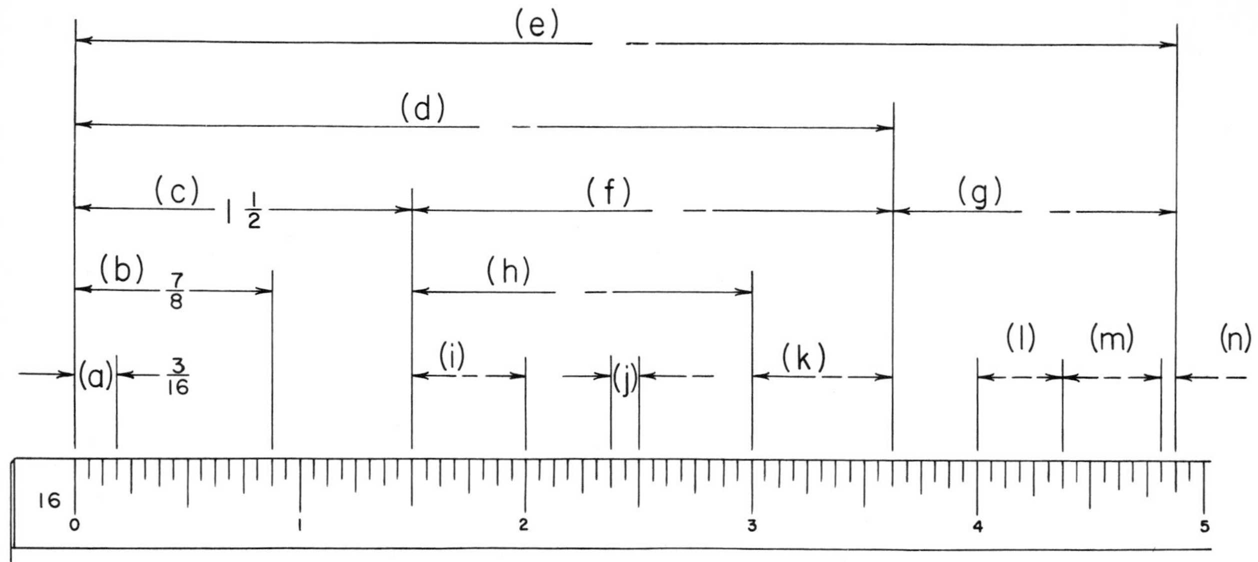

Fig. 1-7. Scale-reading problem.

on the ruler you have used in other classes. Each inch has been sub-divided into sixteenths (the smallest division) with the major markings for 1/8 (2/16), 1/4 (2/8), and 1/2 (2/4) in. By studying Fig. 1-7 closely, you will observe that dimension

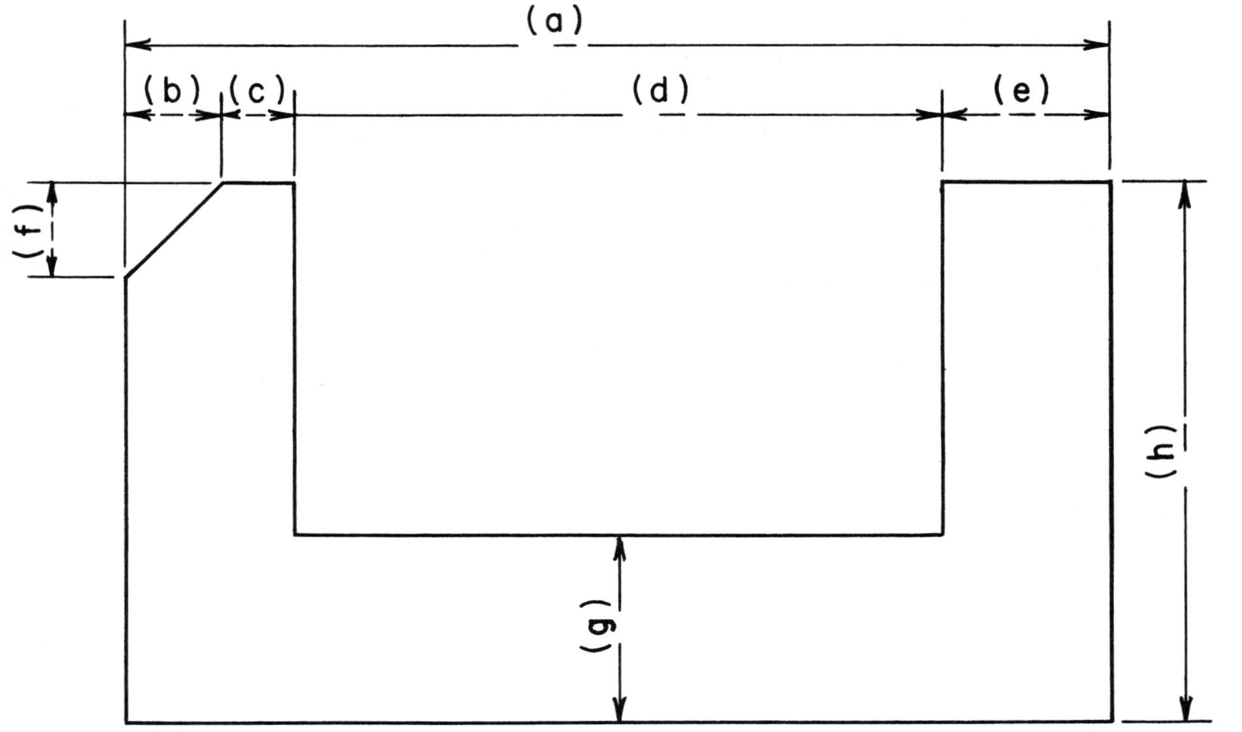

Fig. 1-8. Dimensioning problem.

(a) is equal to 3/16 in., (b) is equal to 7/8 in., and (c) is equal to 1-1/2 in. Try your skill now and complete the reading of the scale.

DRAFTING ACTIVITY

Read dimensions "d" through "n," Fig. 1-7, and write the dimensions on a separate sheet of paper.

Now let's see how well you do with your own scale in the next drafting activity.

DRAFTING ACTIVITY

Measure the length of each line in Fig. 1-8. Write the dimensions on a separate sheet of paper.

Your accuracy in measuring can be improved by eyeing the scale directly from above and using a sharp pencil to make a light mark perpendicular to the scale, Fig. 1-9. Accuracy in laying off a series of measurements along a line can be improved by making these measurements without moving the scale, Fig. 1-10.

The scale is a measuring tool and should never be used as a straight edge in drawing a line. Marking on the scale is a grade school trick and is never done by a good draftsman. Keep your scale clean so that it can easily be read.

FASTENING DRAWING PAPER TO BOARD

The drawing paper may be located anywhere on the board as long as it is aligned with the working edge of the board and T-square. However, you will find that you get best results when your paper is located near the working edge of the drawing board and centered vertically, Fig. 1-11.

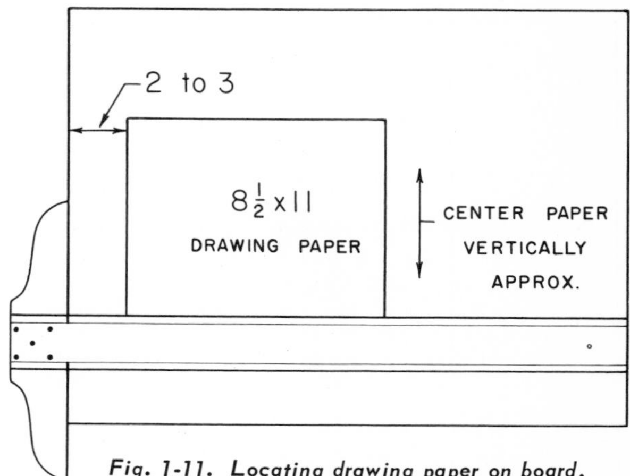

Fig. 1-11. Locating drawing paper on board.

Position the T-square near the lower part of the drawing board, and place the

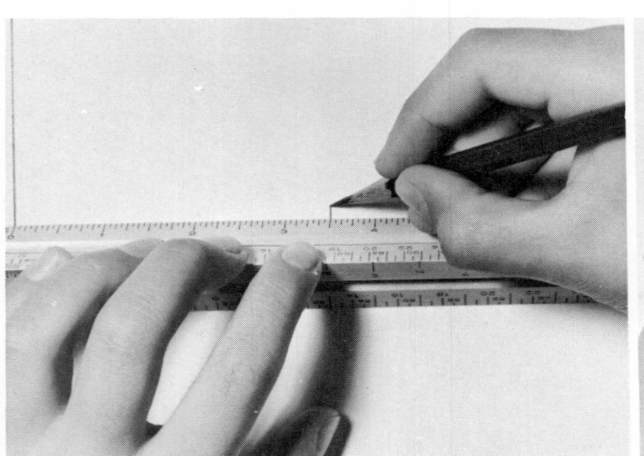

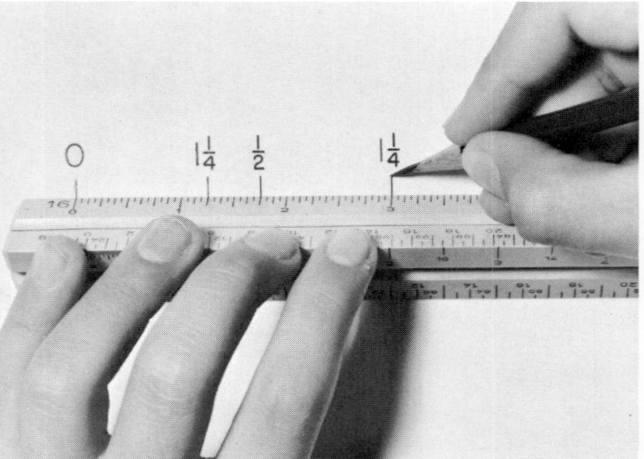

Fig. 1-9. Left. Eye the scale directly from above. Fig. 1-10. Right. Laying off a series of measurements.

paper against the working edge of the T-square, Fig. 1-12. Adjust the T-square and paper to properly position the paper on the board. Fasten with four pieces of drafting tape (or thumb tacks), Fig. 1-12.

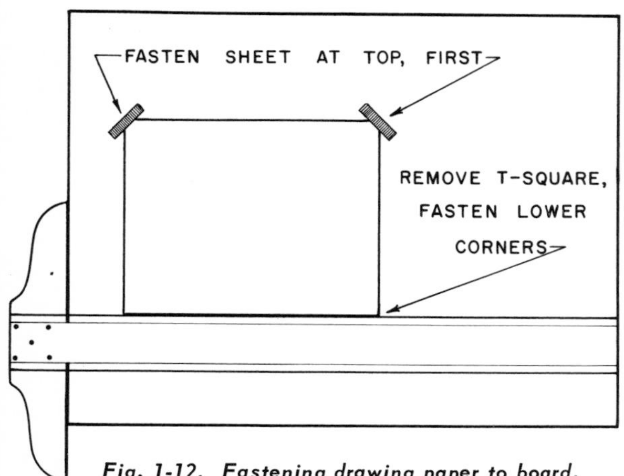

Fig. 1-12. Fastening drawing paper to board.

DRAFTING ACTIVITY

Fasten Plate No. 1 to board.

FORM AND WEIGHT OF LINES

In drafting, lines have a definite form and weight (width). When these are properly constructed, they give meaning and character to your drawing.

Shown in Fig. 1-13 are construction, border, and visible lines.

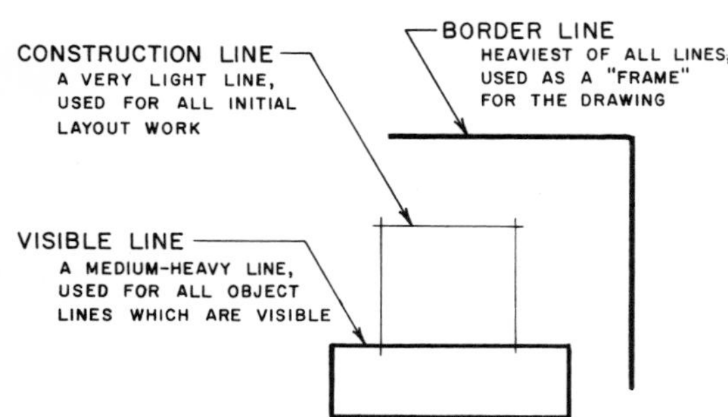

Fig. 1-13. Construction, border, and visible lines.

Construction lines are very light lines which can be easily erased. Use these lines to lay out all work. Later, when you are sure of your work, border lines and visible lines can be darkened to their proper weight.

A complete alphabet of lines used in drafting is shown on page 104.

BORDER AND TITLE BLOCK

A border line is usually drawn around a sheet to serve as a "frame" for the drawing. The border should be drawn very lightly at first and darkened when the plate is completed.

In addition to the border a title block is included on all plates. Architects, draftsmen in industry, and others making drawings include information here to identify and supplement the drawing. Such things as the name of the industry, object drawn, scale of drawing, draftsman's name, checker or supervisor, and date, are included. For your drawings you will want to leave space for the name of your school, title of plate (name of object drawn), scale, date, your name, and plate number. Refer to page 105 for suggested title block layouts.

DRAFTING ACTIVITY

Plate No. 1

Lay out "Plan A" border and title block. Refer to page 105. Unless otherwise directed, all of your plates will be laid out with the "Plan A" border and title block.

Many of the drawing problems in this text will require that your plate be divided into four equal sections, Fig. 1-14c. To divide your plate in this manner, follow this procedure:

1. Lay the scale across your plate with the zero of the scale on the line above the title block with a number easily divisible by 2, such as 12, on the top border line, Fig. 1-14a.

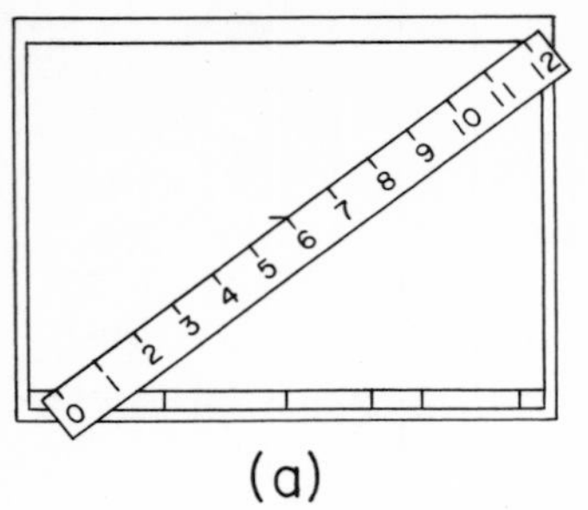

(a)

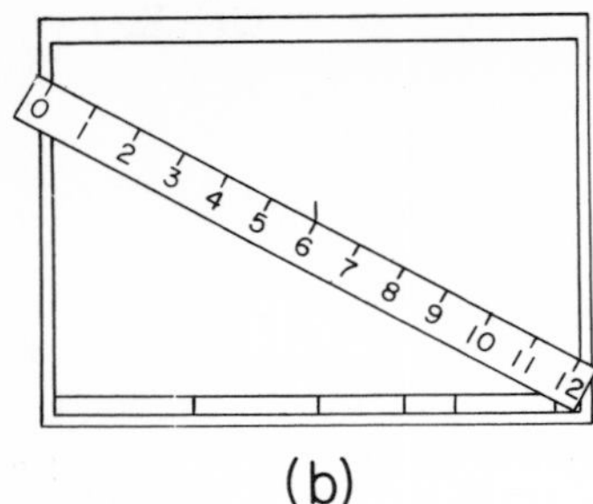

(b)

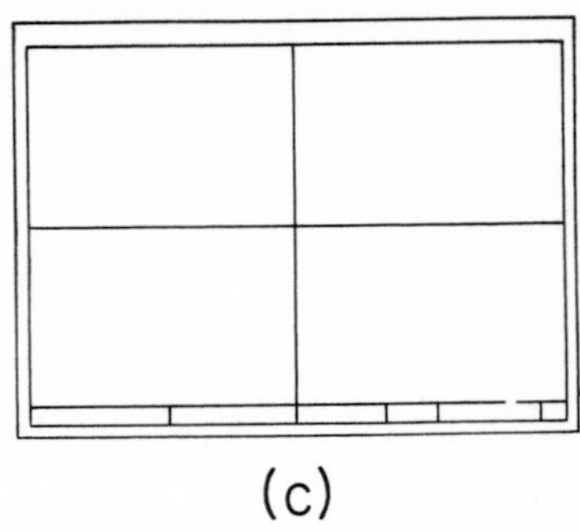

(c)

Fig. 1-14. Dividing plate into four equal parts.

2. At the center point, 6 in., mark a short dash parallel to the horizontal border lines. This is the location for the horizontal dividing line.
3. Follow the same procedure for locating the vertical dividing line, Fig. 1-14b.
4. Draw light lines through these points to divide plate into four equal sections, Fig. 1-14c.

DRAFTING ACTIVITY

Plate No. 1
Divide plate into 4 equal sections.

ERASING PENCIL MARKS AND CLEANING DRAWINGS

Even the best draftsmen find it necessary to erase at times, and when they do, they use the correct eraser and technique for the job. You should have two types of erasers for use in the drafting room: a red rubber eraser for removing lines and other pencil marks, and art gum for cleaning over-all areas of the drawing, Fig. 1-15. An ink eraser which contains abrasives should never be used since it scratches the surface of the drawing paper.

When erasing is necessary, follow this procedure:

1. Clean the eraser by rubbing it on scrap paper before using it on your drawing.
2. With your free hand, hold the drawing firm to avoid wrinkling.
3. If necessary, to protect surrounding area, use an erasing shield, Fig. 1-16.
4. Remove pencil marks with red rubber eraser.
5. Clean plate with art gum before final finishing of lines.

Fig. 1-15. Erasers used in drawing.

6. Dust surface of drawing with brush or cloth after erasing.

The bad effects of erasures can be avoided by drawing all lines in lightly. Remember, erasing will not remove deep pencil grooves in your drawing paper.

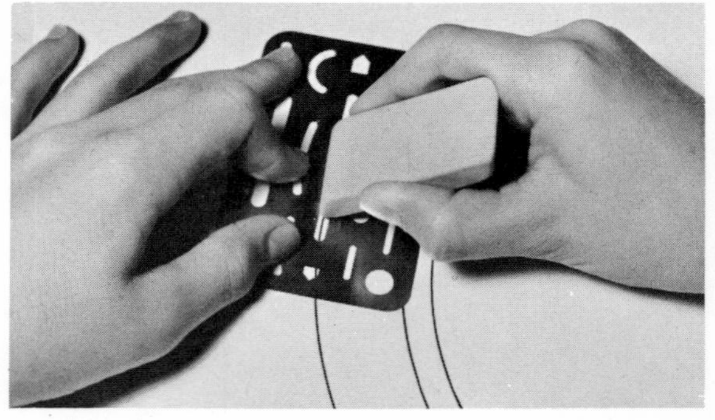

Fig. 1-16. Erasing shield in use.

DRAFTY SAYS: "In layout work use light construction lines."

DRAWING HORIZONTAL LINES

Horizontal lines are drawn from left to right, with the T-square held firmly against the left edge of the drawing board. (Left handers should reverse this procedure.) After the T-square is in position for the line to be drawn, move the left hand to a position on the T-square blade to prevent the T-square from slipping. The pencil is slanted at an angle of 60 deg. to the right, Fig. 1-17, the direction the line is to be drawn. Let the little finger slide along on the T-square as you rotate the pencil between the thumb and forefinger. Rotating the pencil will help you to keep the point sharp, and get a uniform line weight (width).

DRAWING VERTICAL LINES

Vertical lines are drawn toward the top of the board along the vertical edge of either the 30-60 deg. triangle or the 45 deg. triangle. The triangle is held securely against the T-square with the left hand, Fig. 1-18. The pencil is again slanted at a 60 deg. angle in the direction in which the line is being drawn and rotated slowly.

DRAFTING ACTIVITY

Plate No. 1

1. Section A. Draw a series of horizontal lines as shown in Fig. 1-19.
2. Section B. Draw a series of vertical lines as shown in Fig. 1-19.
3. These lines should be drawn lightly at first. When your work has been checked by your instructor, the lines can be darkened to the weight of visible lines.

DRAWING INCLINED LINES

An inclined line is any straight line other than a horizontal or vertical line. It is usually drawn by using one or two triangles in combination with a T-square. By using the triangles separately, or by combining them as shown in Fig. 1-20, any 15 deg. angle from the horizontal or vertical can be drawn. Note the directions in which the lines are drawn as indicated by the arrows, Fig. 1-20.

The triangles can also be used as a straightedge to join two points with a straight line, Fig. 1-21.

DRAFTING ACTIVITY

Plate No. 1

1. Draw inclined lines in sections C and D, as shown in Fig. 1-22.
2. Darken these lines and the border lines to the proper weight.

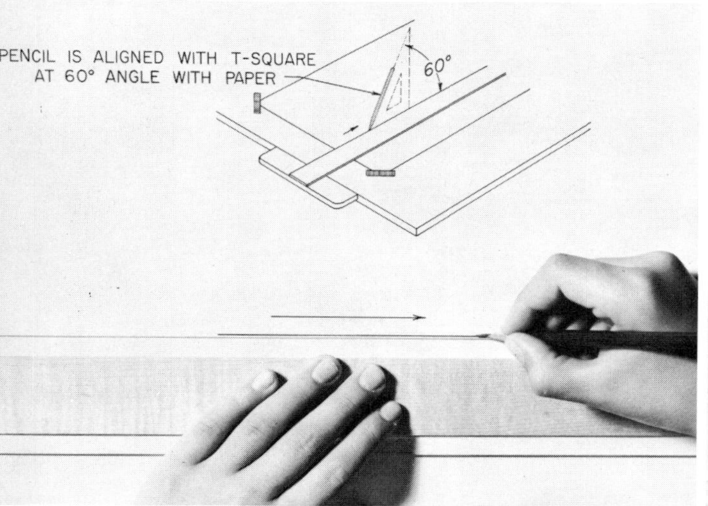

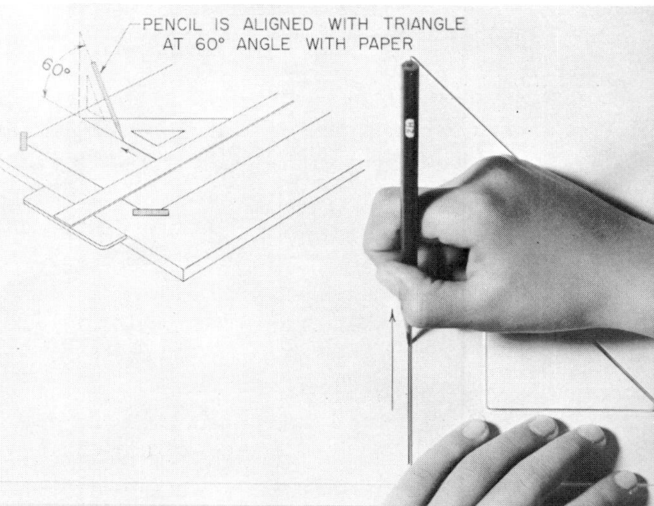

Fig. 1-17. Left. Drawing a horizontal line. Fig. 1-18. Right. Drawing a vertical line.

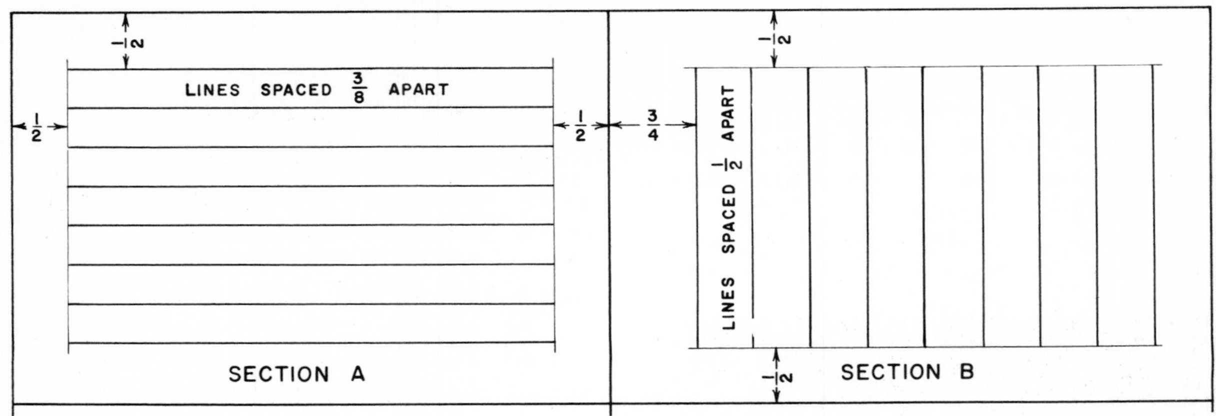

Fig. 1-19. Layout for Sections A and B, Plate No. 1.

Fig. 1-20. Combining triangles to draw 15 deg. and 75 deg. lines with the horizontal.

3. Sign your name in the lower right hand corner of Plate No. 1 and hand to your instructor. (Lettering of a title block will come later.)

THE COMPASS

You have likely used the pencil compass to draw circles in some of your math classes. This same compass could be used in beginning drafting, but compasses which can be adjusted more accurately are often needed. Two types of compasses used

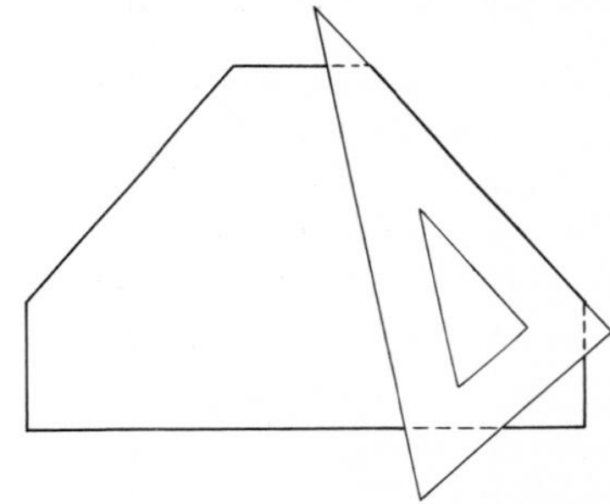

Fig. 1-21. Using the triangle as a straightedge.

Fig. 1-22. Layout for Sections C and D of Plate No. 1.

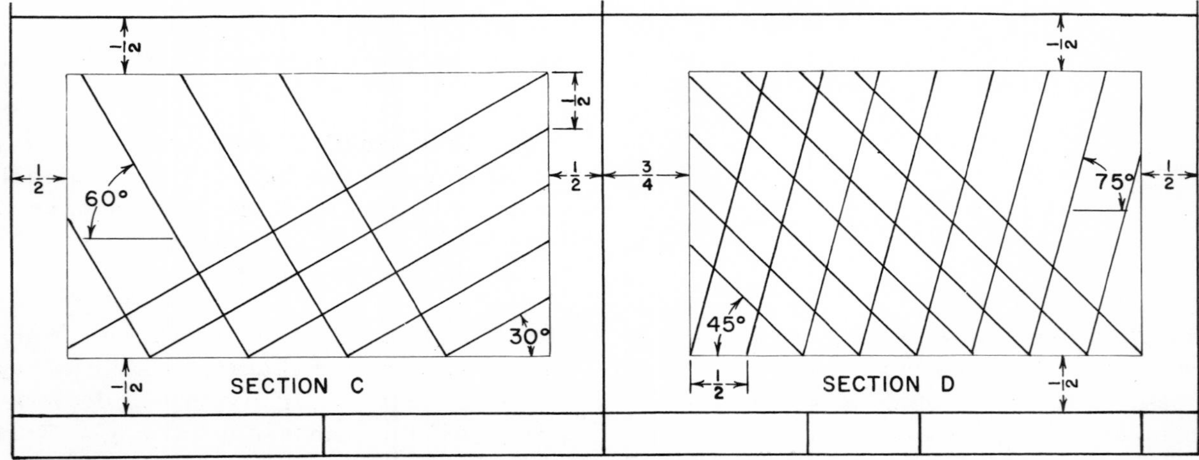

in drafting are the bow pencil with the fine adjusting screw, Fig. 1-23a, and the friction-joint compass usually referred to simply as the compass, Fig. 1-23b. When the radius of the arc or circle is 1 in. or less, use the bow pencil. For an arc or

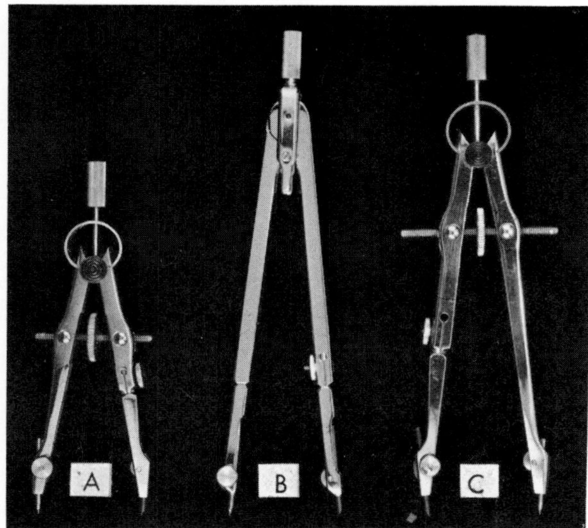

Fig. 1-23. The bow pencil, friction-joint compass, and the large bow pencil.

circle whose radius exceeds 1 in., use compass, or a large bow pencil, Fig. 1-23c. For an arc or circle with radius greater than 2 in., the legs of the compass

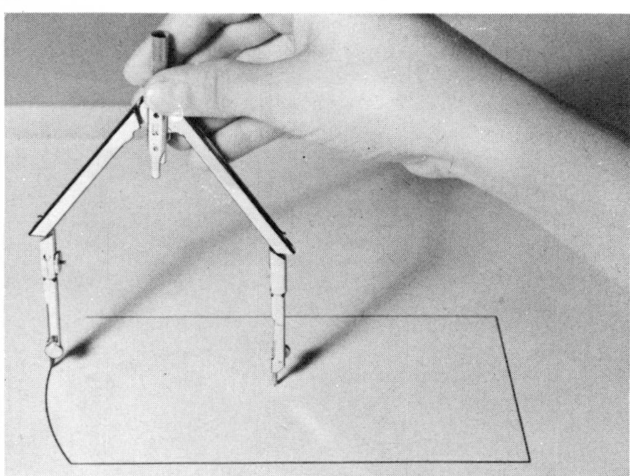

Fig. 1-24. Using compass with the knees bent.

should be bent at the knees and adjusted to meet the paper in a vertical position, Fig. 1-24. Insert the lengthening bar in the compass for a radius greater than 5 in.

SHARPENING COMPASS LEAD

The lead in your compass should be one grade softer than the lead in the drafting pencil you are using for line work. Usually, an F or H grade will give satisfactory results.

Your drafting pencil lead is sharpened to a conical point, but the compass lead

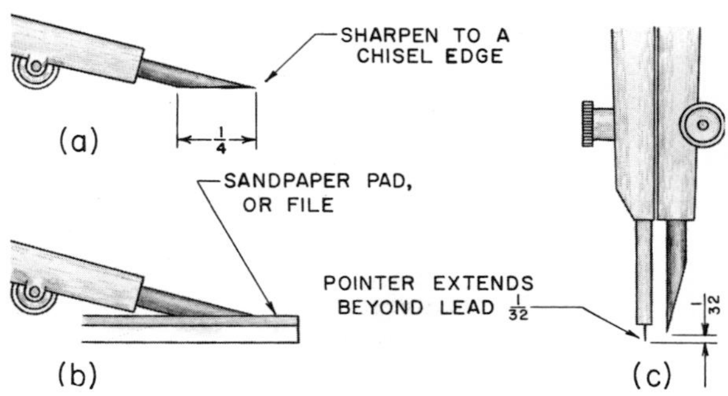

Fig. 1-25. Compass lead has a chisel edge.

is sharpened more like a chisel edge, Fig. 1-25a. Adjust the lead in the compass so that approximately 3/8 in. extends from the compass leg. Sharpen the lead (one side only) on a sandpaper pad or file to form a face of about 1/4 in. in length, Fig. 1-25b. Clean the graphite dust from the lead with a soft cloth. Adjust the compass needle in the other leg of the compass so that the end containing the point with the shoulder extends beyond the lead approximately 1/32 in., Fig. 1-25c.

DRAWING ARCS AND CIRCLES

The bow pencil is adjusted by twisting the adjusting screw between the thumb and the forefinger, Fig. 1-26. The compass is adjusted by spreading the legs with the thumb and second finger, Fig. 1-27.

To set the compass, measure off the radius (1/2 of the diameter) on a scrap piece of paper, or lightly on your drawing, and adjust the compass accordingly. Test

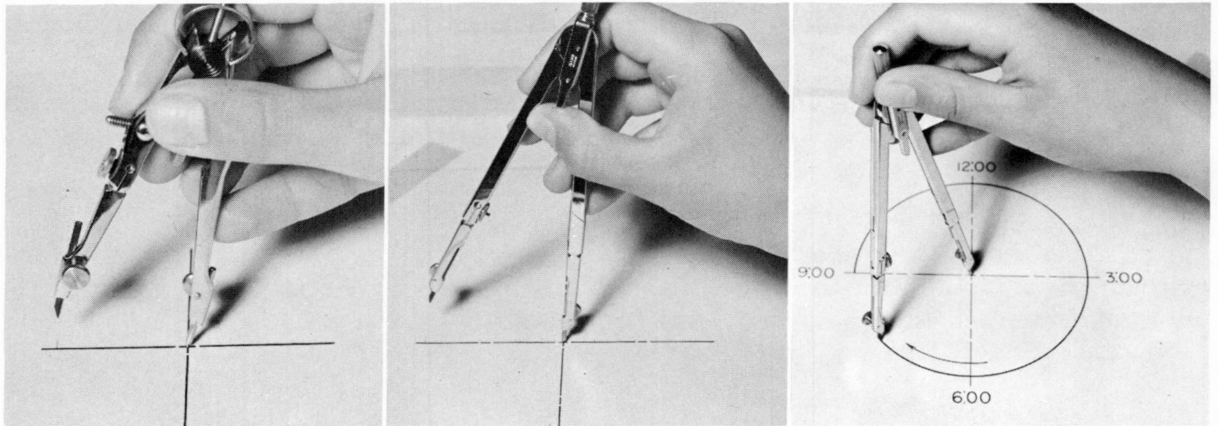

Fig. 1-26. Left. Adjusting the bow pencil. Fig. 1-27. Center. Adjusting the compass. Fig. 1-28. Right. Drawing a circle with the compass.

the setting on scrap paper; check your measurements carefully.

To draw a circle, hold the compass in one hand and start at the "9 o'clock" position, Fig. 1-28, lean the compass slightly forward and revolve in a clockwise direction by rotating the handle between the thumb and forefinger. (Left handers, counterclockwise, starting at 3 o'clock.) Draw circle in lightly until you are sure it is correct.

Refer to Fig. 1-29 and note that an arc is just a part of a circle. Two lines to be joined by an arc are shown in Fig. 1-29a. The center of the arc is located by constructing lines parallel to the lines to be joined, and at a distance equal to the radius of the arc, Fig. 1-29b. Set your compass, and join the two lines with an arc, Fig. 1-29c. Draw the arc lightly until you are sure it is correct.

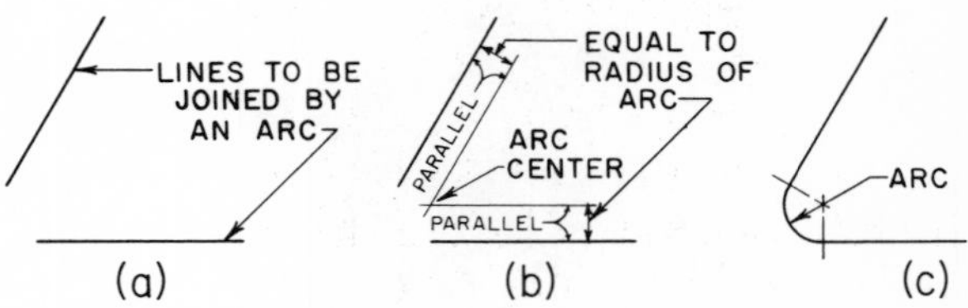

Fig. 1-29. Joining two lines with an arc.

DRAFTING ACTIVITY

Plate No. 2

1. Draw arcs and circles in section A and B, as required in Fig. 1-30.
2. Sign your name on your plate.

Darken all arcs and circles just before straight lines are to be finished. Avoid

Fig. 1-30. Layout for Sections A and B, Plate No. 2.

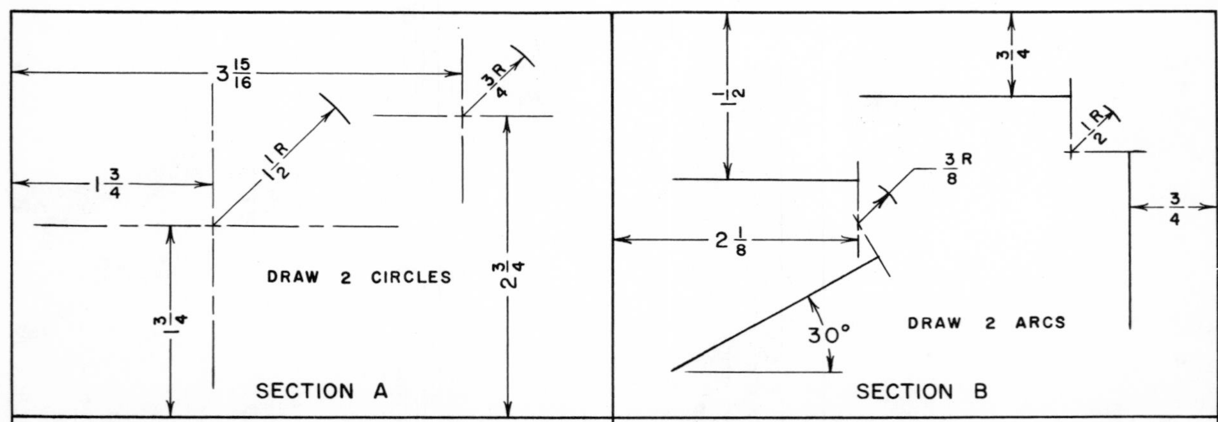

making a large hole in your paper with the compass point.

THE DIVIDERS

Two types of dividers used extensively by draftsmen are similar to the friction-joint compass and the bow pencil; however, the dividers are equipped with a second steel point rather than a pencil, Fig. 1-31. Dividers are used in transferring distances, Fig. 1-32, and in dividing distances equally, Fig. 1-33.

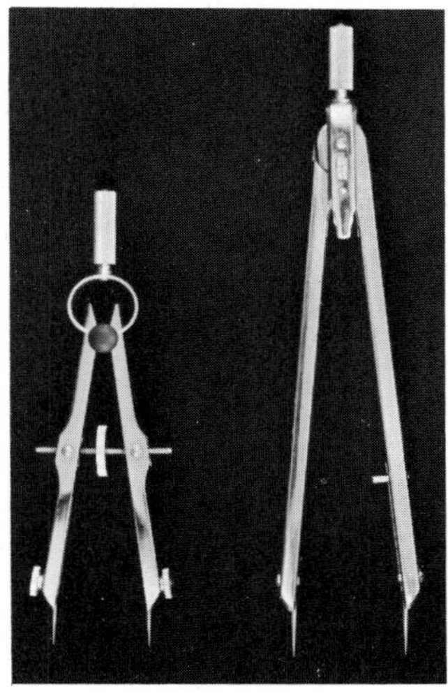

Fig. 1-31. Two types of dividers.

Avoid puncturing the paper with the divider points. Make light dents with the points and, if necessary, mark the place immediately with a sharp pencil.

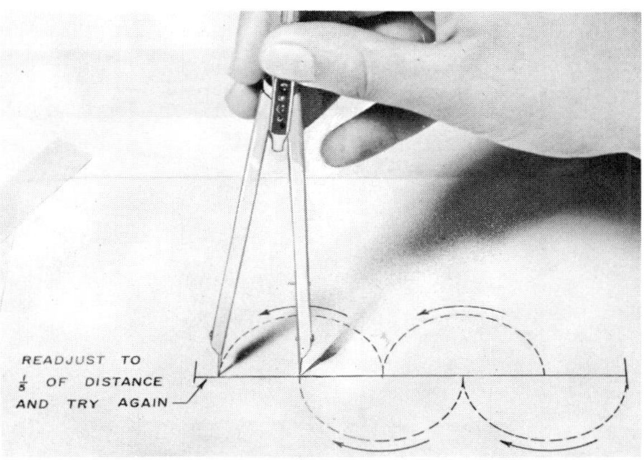

Fig. 1-33. Dividing distances equally with dividers.

DRAFTY SAYS:
"Keep your hands clean."

DRAFTING ACTIVITY

Plate No. 2

Divide the lines in section C as required in Fig. 1-34.

Fig. 1-32. Transferring distances with dividers.

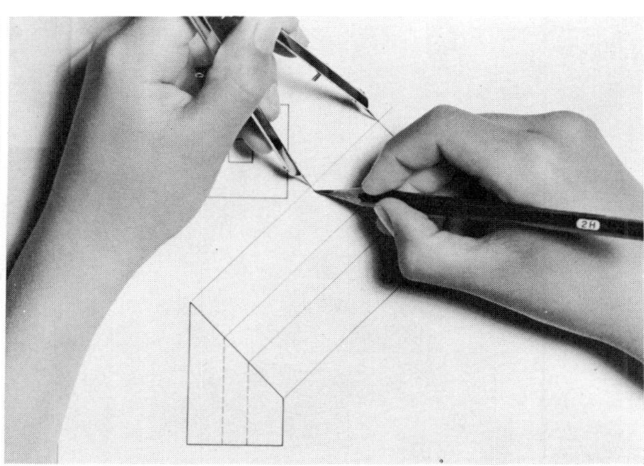

GEOMETRICAL METHOD OF DIVIDING A LINE OR SPACE INTO EQUAL PARTS

There are several ways of dividing a line or space into equal parts. One method, using the dividers, was shown in Fig. 1-33. Another method would be to divide the line mathematically. Still another method which you will find useful in drafting, as well as in your shopwork, is the geometrical method. You have been using this method in dividing your plates into four sections. Now let's see how it works for dividing a line or piece of lumber. The procedure is as follows:

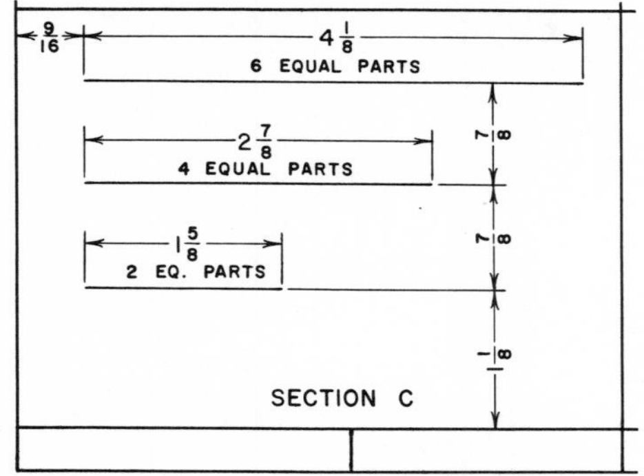

Fig. 1-34. Layout for Section C of Plate No. 2.

1. Line AB = 6-7/16 in. to be divided into five equal parts, Fig. 1-35a.
2. Drop a vertical (perpendicular) line BC down from B, Fig. 1-35b.
3. With the zero on the scale at point A, rotate the scale until a number easily divisible by five, such as 10, crosses line BC, Fig. 1-35b.
4. Mark off the 5 divisions with short dashes parallel to line BC, Fig. 1-35c.
5. Project vertical lines through these points to line AB, Fig. 1-35d.

This same method may be used in dividing a board into equal parts, Fig. 1-36.

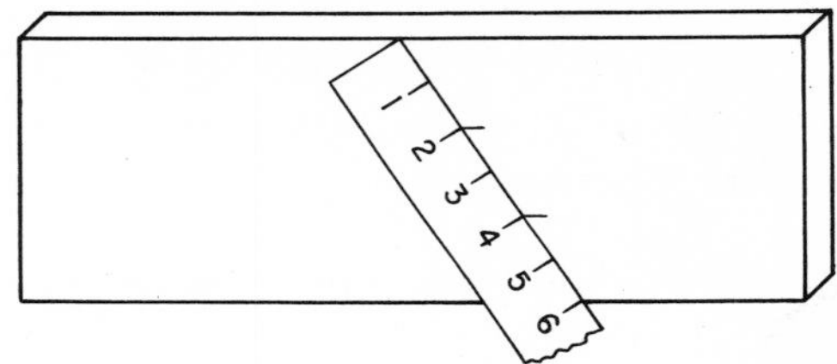

Fig. 1-36. Dividing board into equal parts geometrically.

Fig. 1-35. Geometrical method of dividing a line.

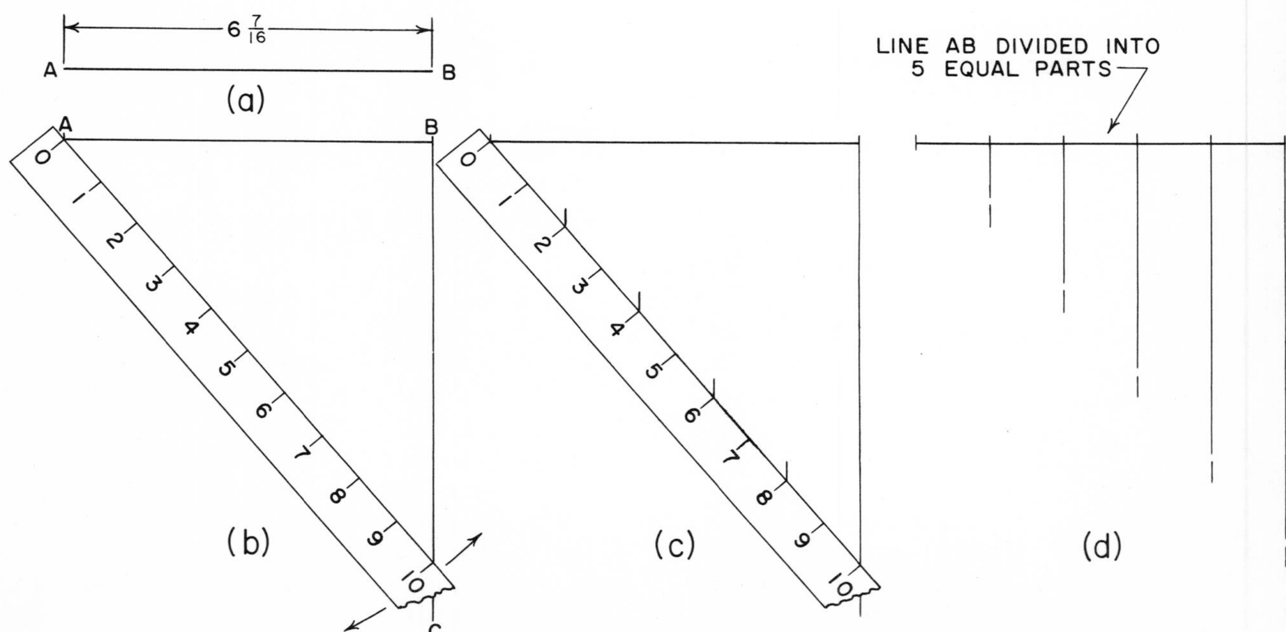

Try your skill at dividing a line by the geometrical method in the next drafting activity.

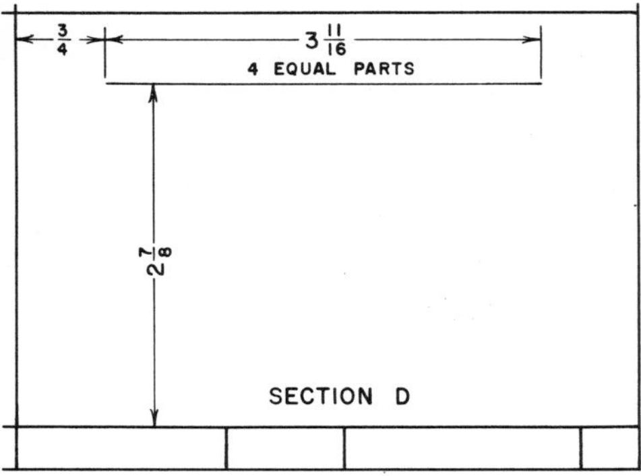

Fig. 1-37. Layout for Section D, Plate No. 2.

DRAFTING ACTIVITY

Plate No. 2

1. Use section D and divide the line as shown in Fig. 1-37.
2. Date the plate.

In addition to your plate layouts, you will use this skill in the solution of some problems in the shop.

DRAWING IRREGULAR CURVES

The draftsman is frequently required to draw curves which are not circles or arcs. These curves are called irregular curves, Fig. 1-38. They should be drawn with

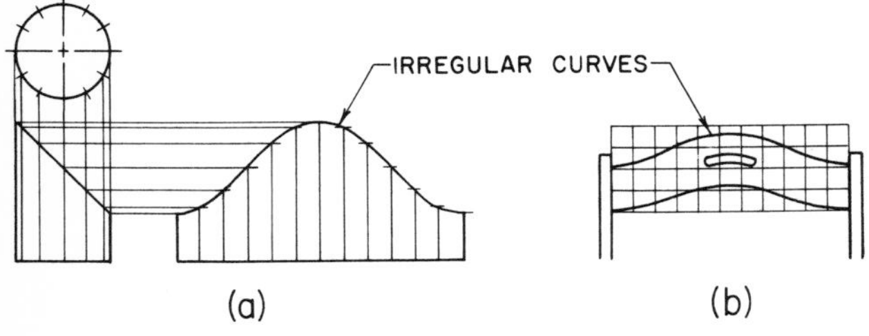

Fig. 1-38. Irregular curves.

smoothness and accuracy. To achieve these qualities, they may be drawn freehand, or with a device called a French curve, or irregular curve, Fig. 1-39.

The procedure for drawing an irregular curve is as follows:

1. Points are established either by projection as in sheetmetal pattern development, Fig. 1-38a, or by the

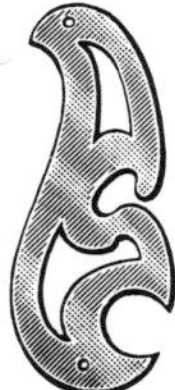

Fig. 1-39. These instruments are called French curves or irregular curves. (Keuffel & Esser Co.)

squares method of enlarging a design, Fig. 1-38b.

2. Sketch a very light freehand curve through these points, Fig. 1-40. (If curve is to be completed by the freehand method, darken the line by letting the eye lead the pencil over the light construction lines. If French curve is to be used, omit freehand

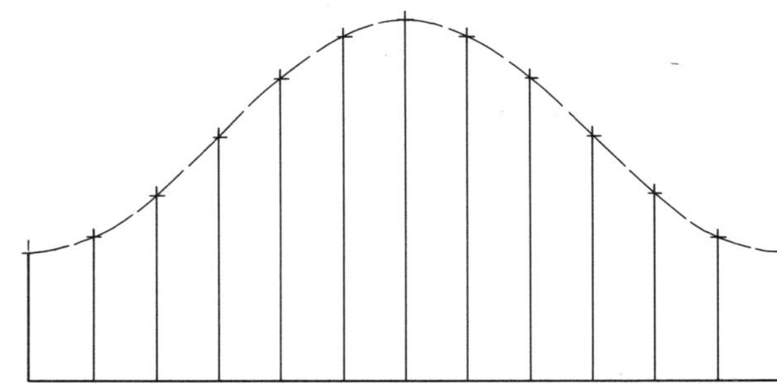

Fig. 1-40. Freehand line sketched through points on an irregular curve.

darkening of line, and continue with Step 3.)

3. Match this curve with the French curve. Try to cover three or more points at each setting, Fig. 1-41.
4. Draw only part of the curve at each setting. Stop before reaching the point of separation, Fig. 1-41.
5. Make each new setting of the curve flow out of the previous setting, Fig. 1-41.

You will get an opportunity to practice this skill in the following section.

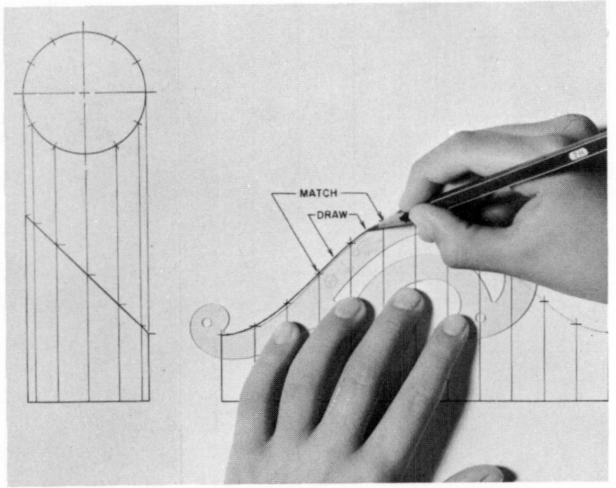

Fig. 1-41. Using the French curve to draw an irregular curve.

ENLARGING A PATTERN BY SQUARES METHOD

Securing a good design for the projects you want to build, either in the school shop or at home, is a real challenge. Such designs can be purchased, created by yourself, or enlarged from small drawings or photographs. You may have occasion to use each of these. Let's consider the method of enlarging by squares, Fig. 1-42.

You may have observed drawings or photographs of designs for projects in magazines or catalogs, and wished that you had a way of enlarging these. Actually, this can be done quite easily. To

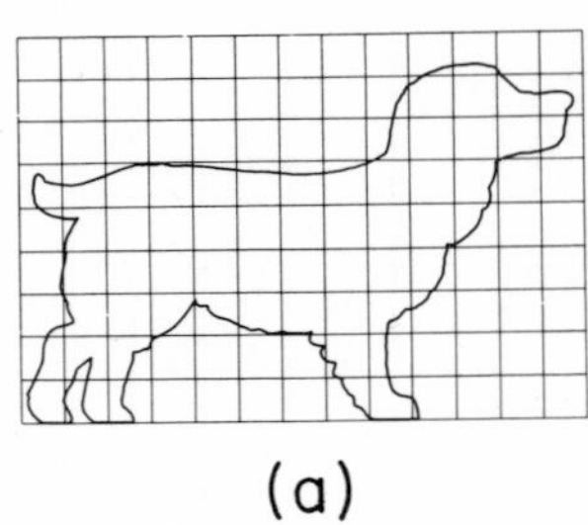

(a)

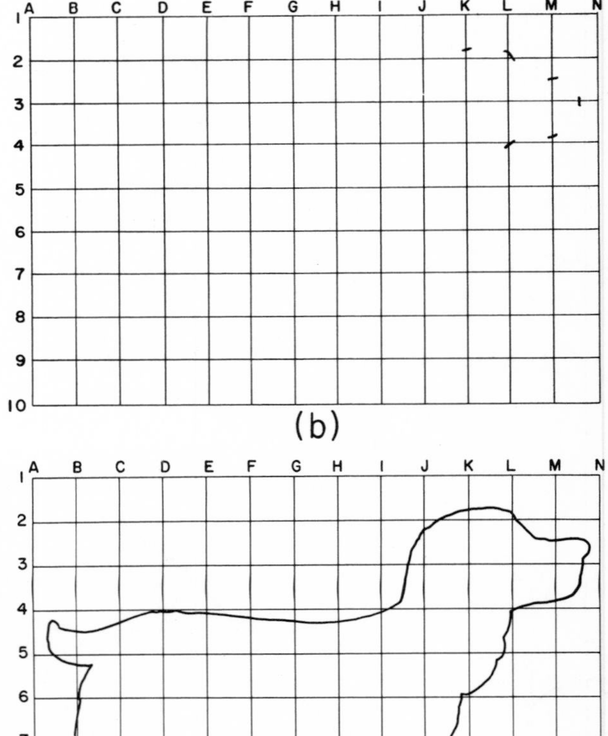

(b)

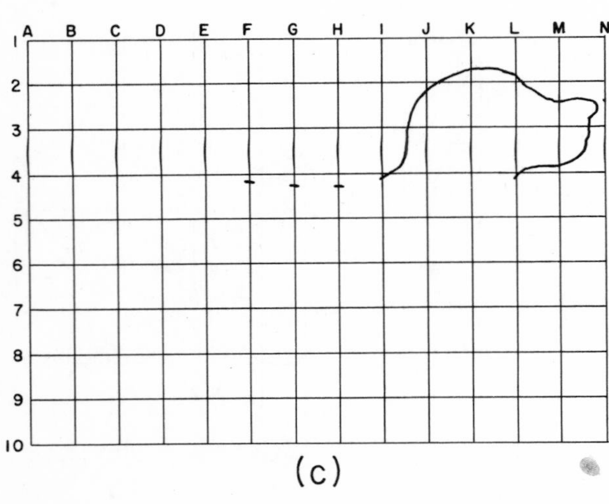

(c)

A B C D E F G H I J K L M N
1 2 3 4 5 6 7 8 9 10

(d)

Fig. 1-42. Enlarging a pattern by the squares method.

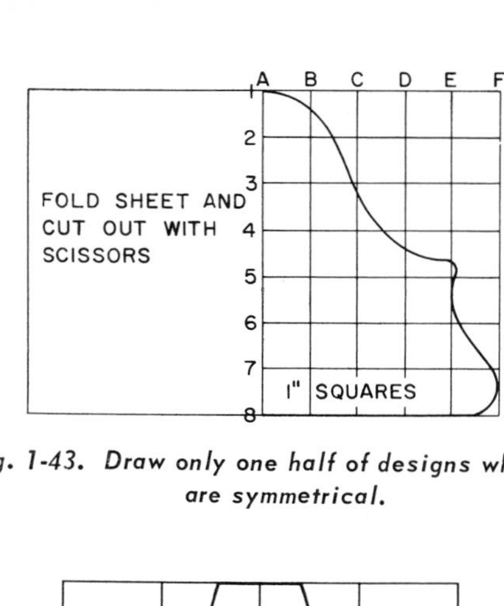

Fig. 1-43. Draw only one half of designs which are symmetrical.

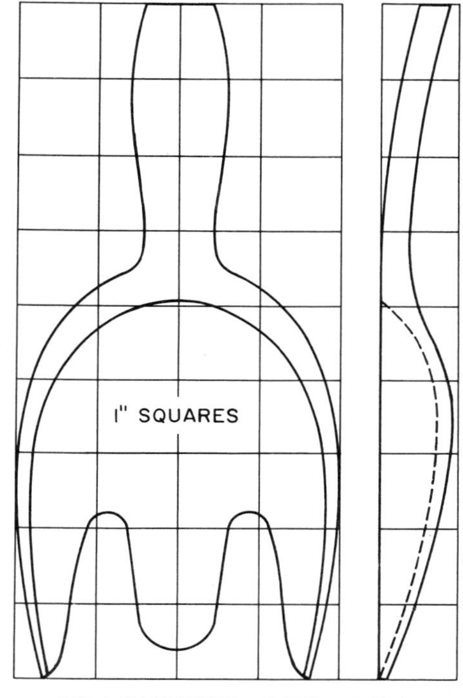

SPAGHETTI SERVERS

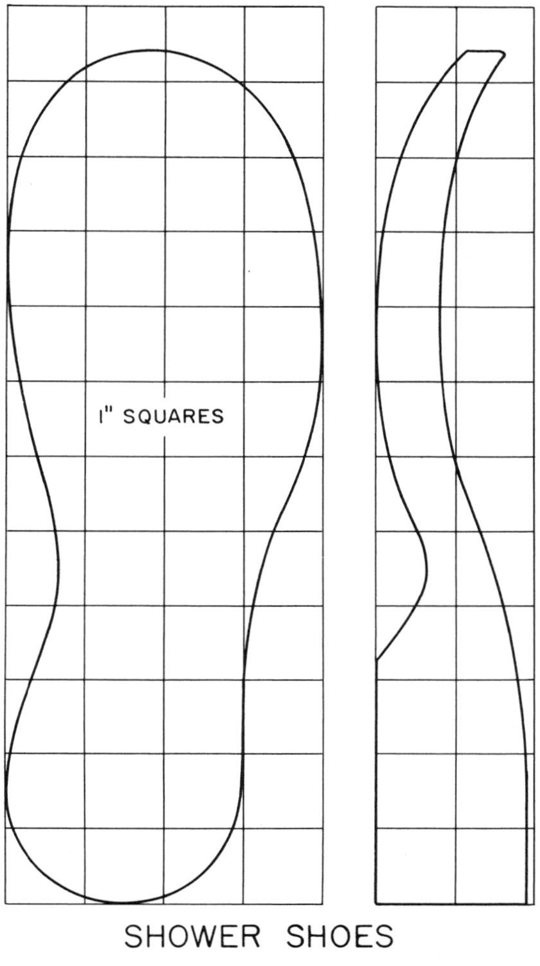

SHOWER SHOES

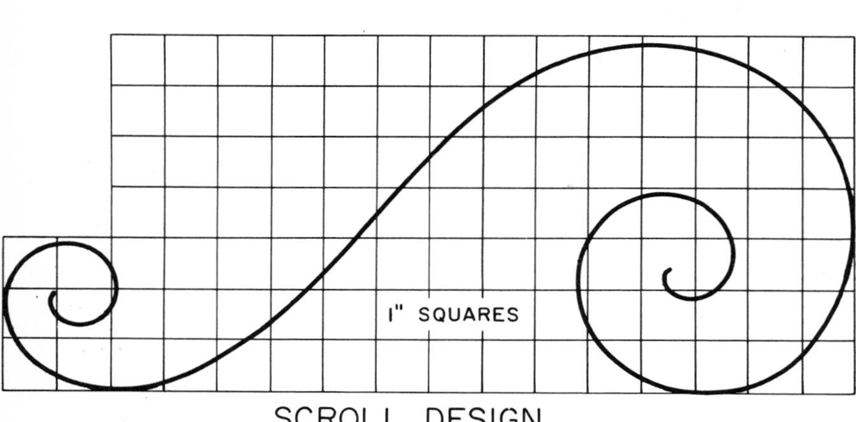

SCROLL DESIGN

BOY SCOUT EMBLEM

Fig. 1-44. Designs to be enlarged.

enlarge a design, follow this procedure:

1. Lay off squares on the design, Fig. 1-42a, or on a piece of transparent paper and place it over the design. On many designs found in books and magazines, squares are already drawn and the size of the enlarged squares are indicated, as in Fig. 1-43. You can control the size of the enlargement by the size of the squares:

Squares on Design	To Enlarge	Squares on Enlargement
1/4 in.	Two times	1/2 in.
1/4 in.	Three times	3/4 in.
1/4 in.	Four times	1 in.

2. Lay off squares of proper size for enlargement on a plain sheet of paper, as shown in Fig. 1-42b. (Use wrapping paper for larger designs.)
3. For convenience in transferring points, number the horizontal lines from top to bottom, and letter the vertical lines from left to right.
4. Start at a prominent point, such as a corner or a projection, on the design and mark the points on the enlarged pattern where the design crosses the numbered and lettered lines. Check your starting point carefully for location, Fig. 1-42b.
5. Mark a few more points and then join them freehand, Fig. 1-42c.
6. Complete the location of points and freehand sketching, Fig. 1-42d. The French curve may be used on some designs to get a smooth curve.
7. To save time in transferring designs which are symmetrical (identical on both sides), draw only one half, fold the paper and transfer the design to the other half by rubbing the back side of the original line with a coin, or cut it out with the scissors, Fig. 1-43.
8. Your pattern is now ready for use. Cut it out and trace it on your material. Transfer it by use of carbon paper; or by a tracer tool if your material is leather.

DRAFTING ACTIVITY

Plate No. 3

Select a design from those shown in Fig. 1-44, or from another book or a magazine, and enlarge by the squares method. Use drawing paper or wrapping paper of appropriate size for the enlargement.

QUIZ - UNIT 1

Write answers on separate sheet of paper. Do not write in book.

1. Drafting is the "language of industry." Explain what is meant by this statement.
2. What changes are necessary in drawings for them to be used in a country where another language is spoken?
3. In what ways are you likely to use the skills you acquire in drafting?
4. Discuss some things you can do to keep your drawings clean and neat.
5. In drawing horizontal, vertical and inclined lines, why is the pencil slanted in the direction the line is to be drawn?
6. Explain why ink erasers should not be used on drawings.
7. Why is it poor practice to use the scale as a straight edge?
8. What are the requirements of a good drawing board?
9. The squares on a design are 1/4 in. How large should the squares in the enlargement be in order to enlarge this design five times?
10. What is the heaviest line used in drafting?

NEW WORDS FOR YOU TO USE

1. Diameter (di-am'e-ter)
2. Graphic (graf'ik)
3. Horizontal (hor-i-zon'tal)
4. Multiview (mul'ti-vu)
5. Projection (pro-jek shun)
6. Radius (ra'di-us)
7. Scale (skal)
8. Technician (tek-nish'an)
9. Vertical (vur'ti-kal)

FREEHAND SKETCHING

1. **What is freehand sketching?**
2. **Where is freehand sketching used?**
3. **What skills are required to make good freehand sketches?**

Freehand sketching is the technique of making a drawing without the use of instruments. It is used frequently by the draftsman as the first step in the making of an instrument drawing and is the principal means by which the skilled worker, the technician, or the engineer presents his ideas to others. You, too, will use sketching in your shopwork at school and at home.

Because sketching is done freehand, you will need only a small amount of equipment: an F or HB pencil, drafting erasers

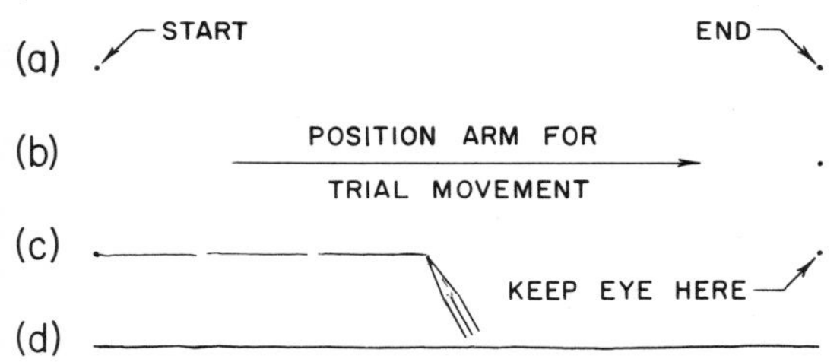

Fig. 2-1. Steps in sketching horizontal lines.

and paper (regular drafting paper, cross sectioned paper, or unruled notebook paper). There are certain skills that must be learned in order to produce good sketches. These skills are the sketching of horizontal, vertical, inclined lines, arcs and circles. Proportion must also be considered.

SKETCHING HORIZONTAL LINES

Horizontal lines are sketched in the following manner:

1. Locate the starting and ending points of the line, Fig. 2-1a.
2. Make several trial movements to position arm, take short strokes from left to right (left handers right to left) keeping eye on end point, Fig. 2-1b.
3. Sketch short light lines at first, Fig. 2-1c (no fuzzy scratches). This will help you control the direction of the line. The line appears as broken sections in the construction stage.
4. Darken the line using one continuous stroke, Fig. 2-1d. To do this, let your eyes lead your pencil along the light construction line.

DRAFTING ACTIVITY

Plate No. 4

1. Lay out border, title block, and divide plate into four sections with instruments.
2. Sign your name on your plate.
3. In section A, sketch three horizontal lines lightly between the points, as shown in Fig. 2-2. Do not darken these lines.

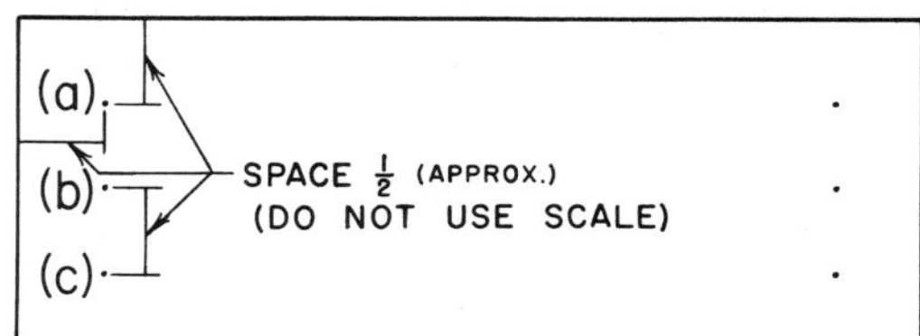

Fig. 2-2. Layout for section A, Plate No. 4.

Are the lines straight? Do they end at the desired points? Were they constructed in short sections?

In the drafting activity which follows, you will sketch additional horizontal lines in the remaining space of Section A. Remember, this is freehand sketching--no scales allowed. Follow the same procedure as for lines a, b, and c; then darken these lines forming straight continuous lines. Your lines should be uniform in weight (width and darkness). It is not expected tnat freehand lines will be as straight as mechanical lines, but a good draftsman will strive for neatness and accuracy in sketching, too.

DRAFTING ACTIVITY

Plate No. 4

In section A, sketch additional horizontal lines and darken.

Are these lines straight? Are they uniform in weight?

SKETCHING VERTICAL LINES

The sketching of vertical lines is quite similar to the sketching of horizontal lines--only the direction of arm movement changes to a downward movement toward the body.

The procedure is as follows:

1. Locate the starting and ending points, Fig. 2-3a.

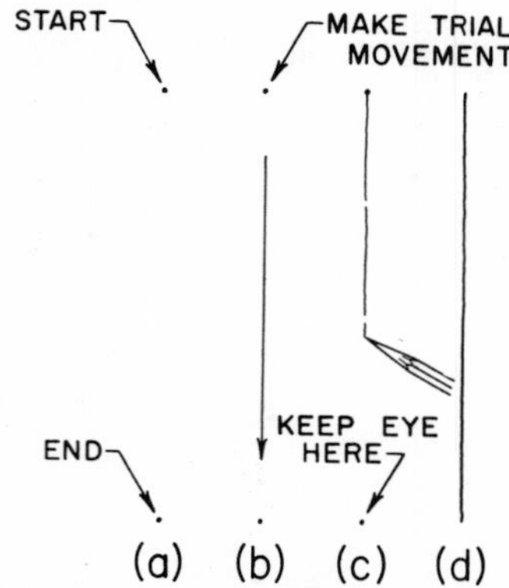

Fig. 2-3. Steps in sketching vertical lines.

2. Without marking your paper, make trial arm movements between top and bottom points to position arm (it will help to line the points up by sight), Fig. 2-3b. Use a pulling arm and finger movement in sketching.
3. Sketch short, light lines at first, Fig. 2-3c, and keep your eye on the point at which the line is to end.
4. Darken the line to form one continuous line of uniform weight, Fig. 2-3d. To do this, let your eye lead your pencil along the light construction line.

DRAFTING ACTIVITY

Plate No. 4

1. In section B, sketch vertical lines between the three sets of points: a, b, and c, as shown in Fig. 2-4.
2. Sketch the lines lightly.

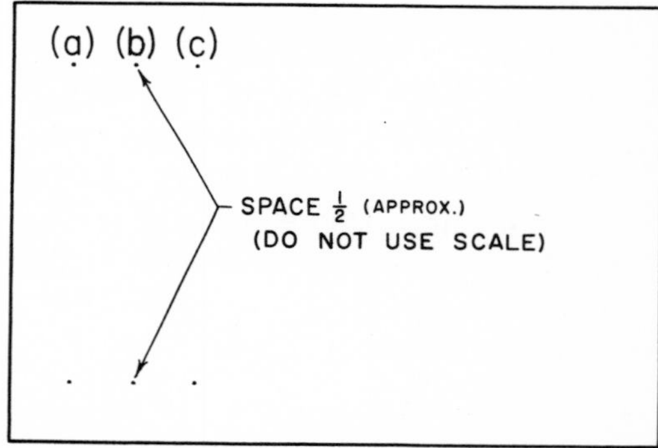

Fig. 2-4. Layout for Section B, Plate No. 4.

Check your lines for straightness. Are the short strokes of the construction lines observable? Try to improve your skill in sketching vertical lines by sketching the lines in the next drafting activity.

DRAFTING ACTIVITY

Plate No. 4

1. Locate additional sets of points for vertical lines in section B by approximating spacing similar to lines a, b, and c.
2. Follow the same procedure as for lines a, b, and c; darken these lines.

Are your lines straight? Are they uniform in weight?

Vertical lines may be sketched as horizontal lines when it is convenient to rotate the paper.

SKETCHING INCLINED LINES

As indicated in Unit I, inclined lines include all straight lines other than horizontal and vertical. If their position is more horizontal than vertical, they should be sketched as horizontal lines--from left to right. If their position is more nearly vertical, sketch them as vertical lines--from top downward. When possible, the paper may be rotated for convenience in sketching.

DRAFTING ACTIVITY

Plate No. 4

1. In section C, follow the procedure for sketching horizontal or vertical lines, and sketch inclined lines between the three sets of points (a-a', b-b', c-c') as shown in Fig. 2-5.
2. Sketch the lines lightly.

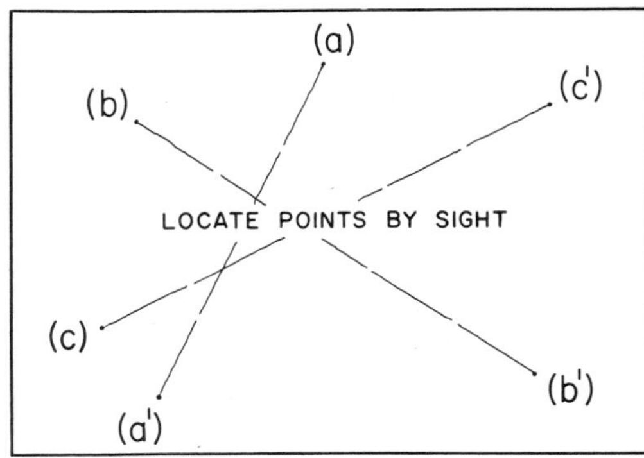

Fig. 2-5. Layout for Section C, Plate No. 4.

Check your lines for straightness and uniformity of line weight.

DRAFTING ACTIVITY

Plate No. 4

1. Lay out additional sets of points for inclined lines in section D.
2. Sketch lines between these points and darken.
3. Date your plate.

SKETCHING ARCS AND CIRCLES

The ability to sketch arcs and circles is essential for the draftsman doing freehand sketching. You, too, will find it to your advantage to develop this skill. Arcs and circles may be neatly sketched by using the following procedure:

1. Sketch center lines of the arcs or circles, Fig. 2-6a.
2. Locate points in the radius (use scrap of paper or pencil as gauge), Fig. 2-6b.
3. Make trial movements between points using a radial arm and wrist movement and include at least three points in each movement, Fig. 2-6c.
4. Sketch light arc in a clockwise or downward movement, depending on position (paper may be rotated for convenience), Fig. 1-6d. Keep eye on the next point, Fig. 2-6e.
5. Sketch complete arc or circle lightly.
6. Darken arc or circle with uniform dense line, let the eye lead the pencil along the light construction line, Fig. 2-6f.

DRAFTING ACTIVITY

Plate No. 5

1. Sketch border, title block, and lines to divide plate into four sections.

DRAFTY SAYS: "Remove erasure dust from drawing with brush or soft cloth."

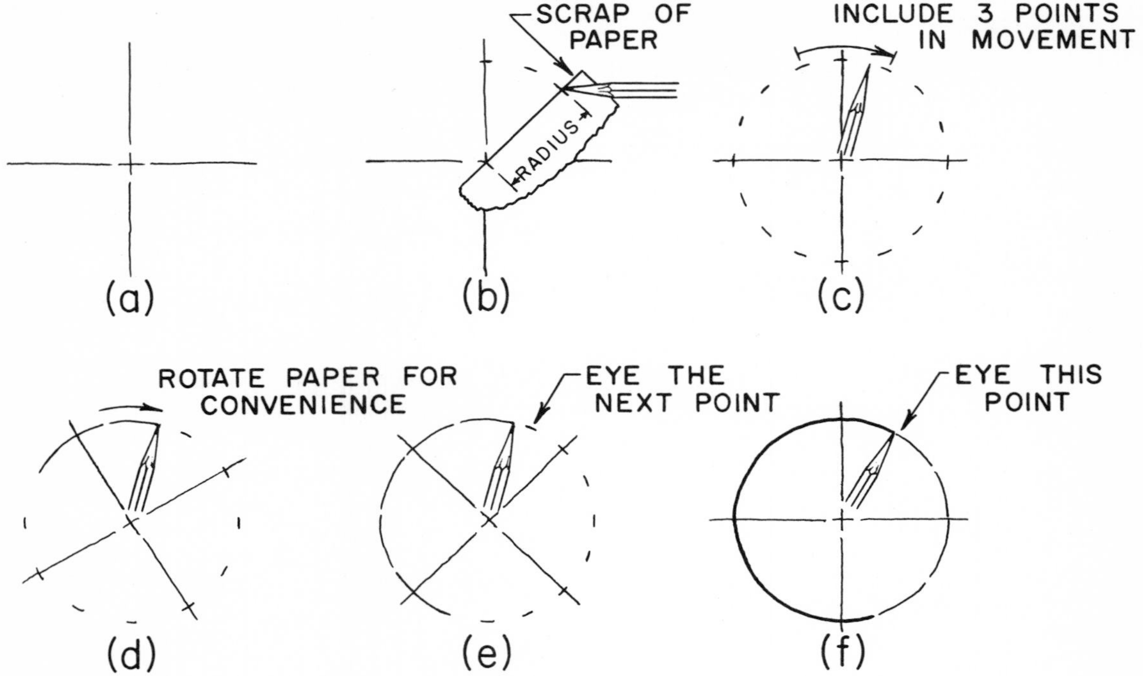

Fig. 2-6. Steps in sketching circles.

2. Write your name on your plate.
3. In section A, sketch circles around points "a" and "b" as shown in Fig. 2-7.

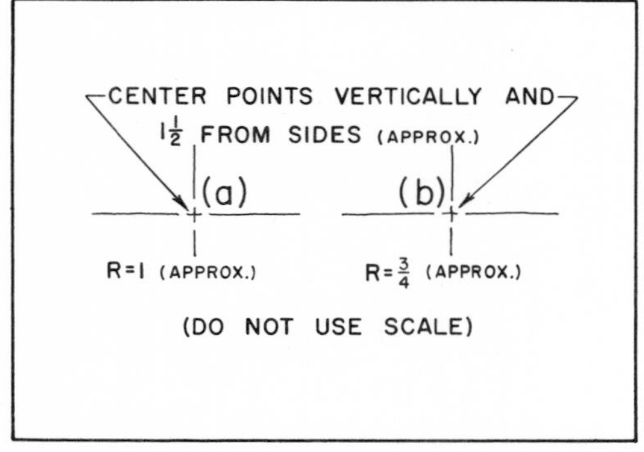

Fig. 2-7. Layout for section A, Plate No. 5.

4. Sketch circle "a" and leave light construction lines.
5 Sketch circle "b" and darken.

Are the circles true and uniform around their centers? Does circle "a" show light construction lines in sections? Is circle "b" uniform in line weight?

In many sketching problems, it is necessary to sketch arcs at corners or between two lines. Let's see if you can apply what you have learned in sketching circles to sketching arcs. Two lines to be joined by an arc are shown in Fig. 2-8a. You remember that the center of an arc is located

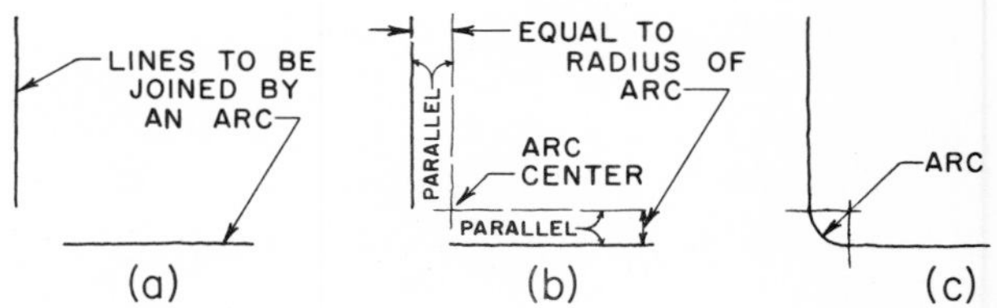

Fig. 2-8. Steps in sketching arcs.

by sketching construction lines parallel to the lines to be joined with the arc, Fig. 2-8b. The radius points may be laid out with a scrap of paper and sketched in the same manner as for a circle, Fig. 2-8c.

DRAFTING ACTIVITY

Plate No. 5

1. In section B, sketch two arcs connecting lines shown in Fig. 2-9.

2. Show construction lines in locating centers of arcs and darken arcs.

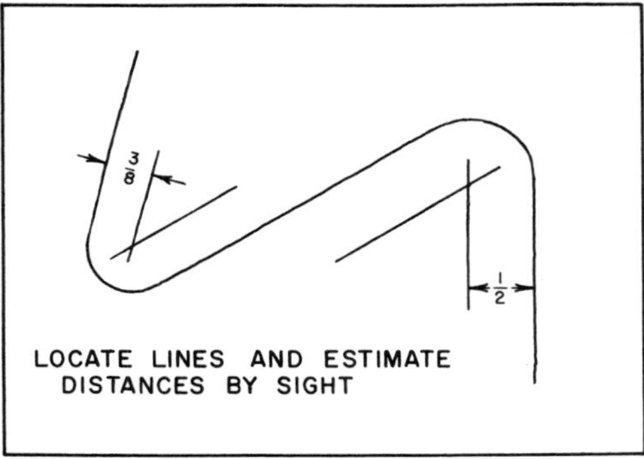

Fig. 2-9. Layout for section B, Plate No. 5.

Are the arcs true? Is the line weight uniform?

PROPORTION IN SKETCHING

So far, you have learned something about the techniques of sketching straight lines, arcs, and circles. With additional experience, you should be able to execute these procedures with considerable ease and skill.

There is another important element, however, in sketching objects consisting of straight lines, arcs, and circles; that is, proportion. If a square is to look like a square, it must have equal, or nearly equal, sides. If a sketch of a table is to resemble a table and have value, then the height and width of the sketch must be proportional.

Remember the object of freehand sketching is to develop skill in drafting without the use of instruments; therefore, you must develop the technique of getting proportion in your sketches without the use of a scale. (Many draftsmen carry a small pocket rule which they use as a straightedge and for measuring purposes in freehand sketching, but they also have the ability to sketch and to gauge proportion without its use.)

Your pencil may be used as a gauge in checking the sides of a square or other geometric form. A scrap of paper may also be used. There are other means of gauging proportion which your instructor may want to show you if time permits.

DRAFTING ACTIVITY

Plate No. 5

1. In section C, sketch a square having sides of approximately 2 in. in length, Fig. 2-10.
2. Fstimate distances and spacing by sight. Do not use a scale.

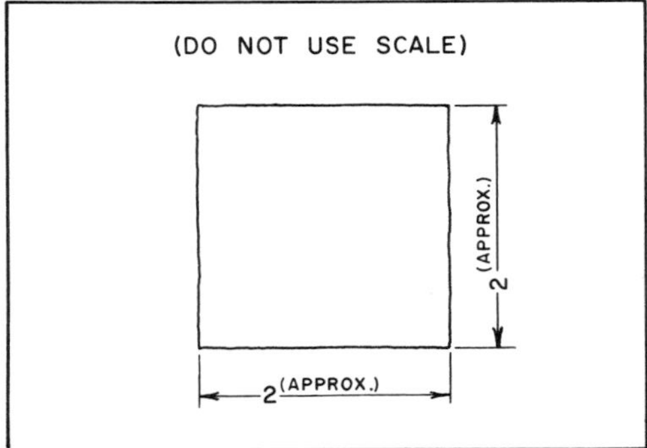

Fig. 2-10. Layout for section C, Plate No. 5.

Are the sides equal? Are the corners square?

DRAFTING ACTIVITY

Plate No. 5

1. In section D, sketch a right triangle (one with a 90 deg. angle) having a base of approximately 1-1/2 in. in length, Fig. 2-11.
2. Estimate distances and spacing by sight. Do not use a scale.

AIDS IN SKETCHING

In many cases you will be making freehand sketches without the use of instruments. However, when aids are available they can be used to improve the sketching technique.

1. When sketching a straight line parallel to the edge of the paper or board, use the edge for a guide and your finger as a gauge.
2. When sketching a straight line, a folded piece of paper makes a good straightedge.

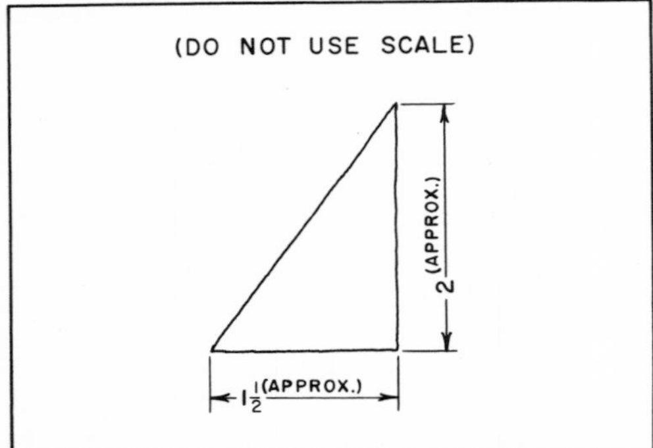

Fig. 2-11. Layout for section D, Plate No. 5.

3. When sketching a 90 deg. angle, a piece of paper may be folded across the straightedge to form a right angle.
4. When sketching a 45 deg. angle, a right angle corner can be folded diagonally.
5. A scrap piece of paper is helpful when sketching equal distances, such as radius points for a circle. Your pencil with its lettering also makes a good measuring device.
6. A small 6 in. pocket rule comes in handy, both for straightedge work and for measuring.
7. A string-and-pencil compass has been used for a long time to make arcs and circles.

These are aids to freehand sketching and should not be confused with instrument drafting. You should first learn the freehand techniques discussed in this unit without using the above aids so that you will be prepared when aids are not available. Later, when quality and speed can be improved with the use of aids and they are available, they may be used. In the next unit on working drawings, you will begin to use your sketching ability.

QUIZ - UNIT 2

1. What is the value of sketching to the draftsman?
2. What equipment is needed to do freehand sketching?
3. How can you improve the straightness and direction of horizontal, vertical, and inclined lines in freehand sketching?
4. What is proportion in sketching? Of what importance is it?
5. Suggest some uses which you can make of the freehand sketching technique.
6. What are some aids which may be used in sketching? When should you make use of these?

NEW WORDS FOR YOU TO USE

1. Approximate (a-prok'si-mit)
2. Clockwise (klok'wiz)
3. Gauge (gaj)
4. Parallel (par'a-lel)
5. Proportion (pro-por'shun)
6. Uniform (u'ni-form)

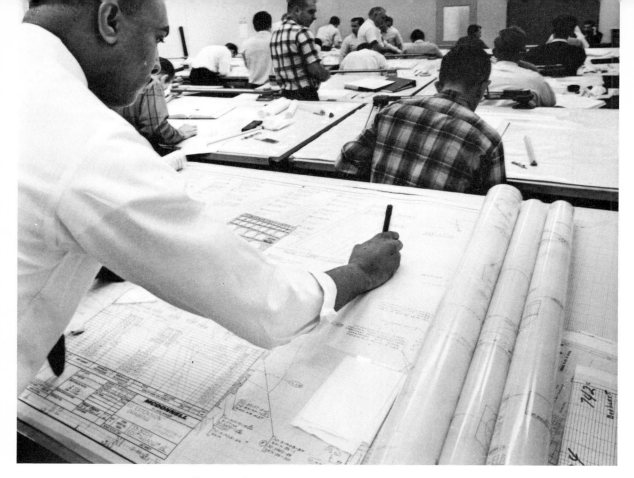

Fig. 3-1. Preparing a working drawing in industry. (McDonnell-Douglas Corp.)

WORKING DRAWINGS

1. What is a working drawing?
2. What is orthographic projection?
3. Is drafting in your future?

Of all the types of drawings made by the draftsman, the working drawing is the one most frequently used. As the name implies, it is the drawing from which the craftsman gets the information he needs in the construction or servicing of an object, Fig. 3-1. He readily sees the shape, size, and details of the object, IF he can read the "language of industry."

In this unit you will begin making working drawings of objects. First, let's see how the different views of a working drawing are obtained.

ORTHOGRAPHIC PROJECTION

Let's take a simple object and imagine that it is placed in a hinged glass box

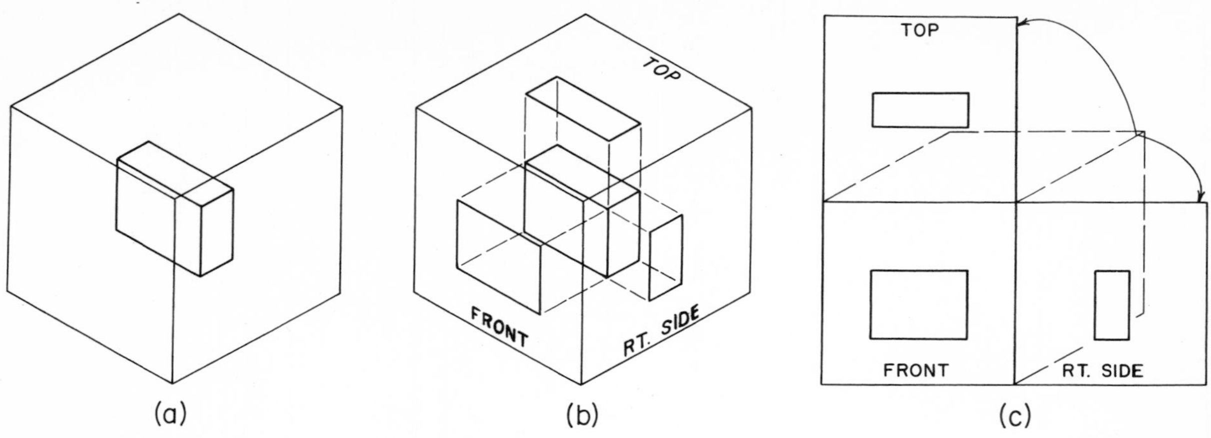

Fig. 3-2. The "glass" projection box in use.

(projection box), Fig. 3-2a. Imagine, also, that the views of the object are projected to the front, top, and right sides of the glass box (planes of projection), Fig. 3-2b. Now fold the top and right-side planes in line with the front plane, Fig. 3-2c. This type of projection is called orthographic projection which means perpendicular or right-angle projection. It also means that the top view is always directly above the front view, and the right-side view (sometimes called right-end view) is always to the right of the front view and in line with it.

As many as six views may be obtained in this manner (the others would be left-side, rear, and bottom views). However, you should draw only those views that are necessary to describe the object clearly.

If you were going to lay out a tennis court, Fig. 3-3, one view would be sufficient. One view is all that is needed to describe certain objects to be made in the shop such as a template (pattern), Fig. 3-4a, or cutting board, Fig. 3-4b, where

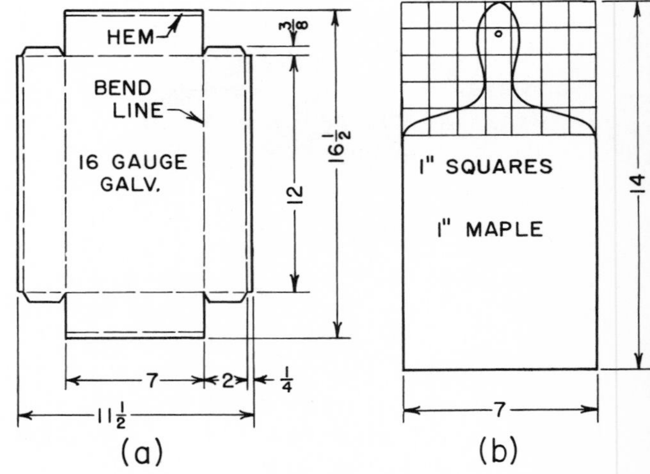

Fig. 3-4. One-view shop drawings.

the thickness of the material can be indicated in a note.

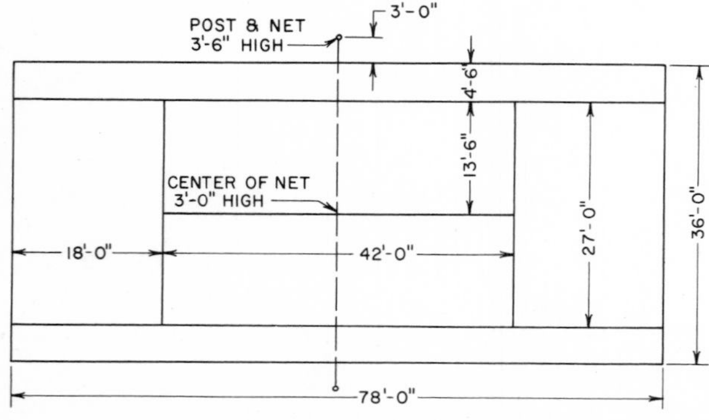

Fig. 3-3. One view of a tennis court is sufficient.

For most cylindrical objects, two views are sufficient. In Fig. 3-5, the right-side

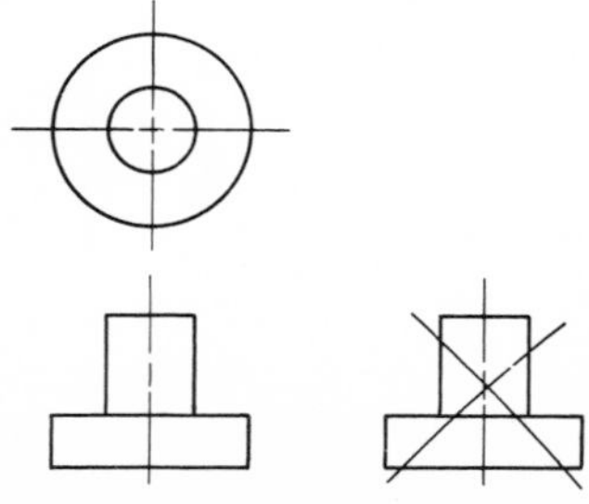

Fig. 3-5. Draw only the necessary views.

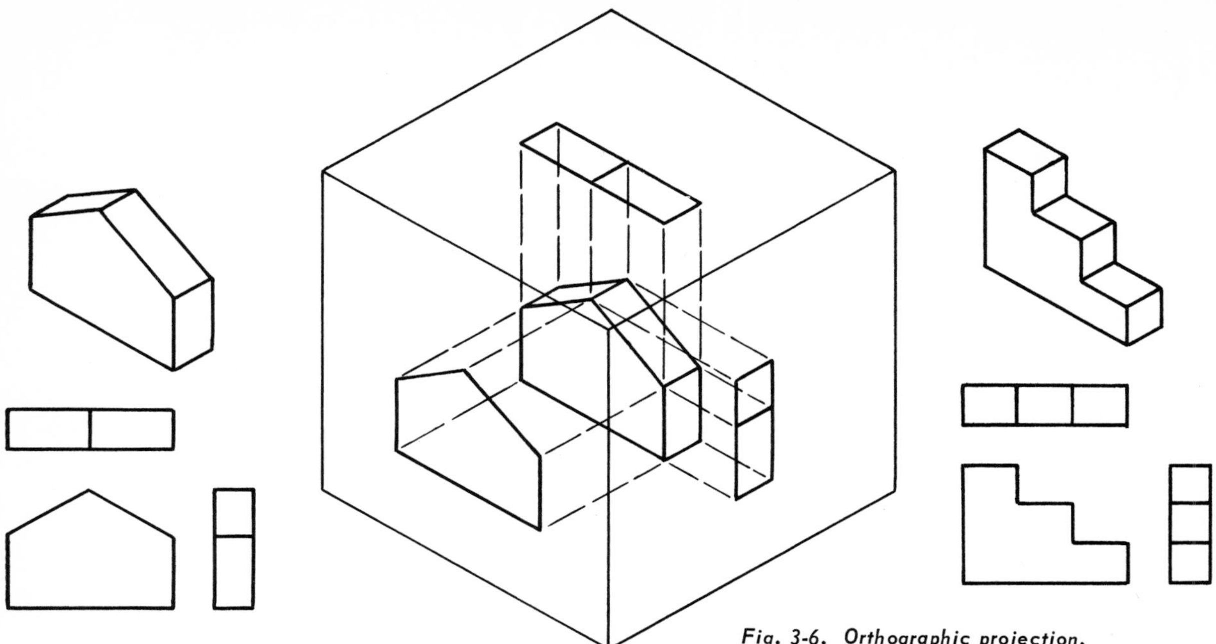

Fig. 3-6. Orthographic projection.

view is identical to the front view. Again, show only the number of views necessary to clearly describe the object--no more. When two or more views are shown, the drawing is sometimes referred to as a multiview drawing.

Nearly all of the projects which you will make in the school shop or at home will require three views to describe adequately the details of their construction.

Two objects are shown in Fig. 3-6, to help you visualize the way in which multiviews are obtained. When you have learned this technique, you are well on your way to understanding multiview drawing. Study the objects and views carefully and make certain NOW that you understand the projection techniques.

Let's see how well you have learned this technique. Fig. 3-7 shows four more blocks. These blocks are quite different in their pictorial views. One block has been drawn correctly in the multiview drawing in Fig. 3-7. If multiview drawings were made of the other three blocks, which of their views would be exactly like those shown?

Study the pictorial views carefully and, on a separate sheet of paper, draw a form similar to the one in the next column.

Indicate with check marks (✓) the views which would be correct for each block and with zeros (0) the views which would be incorrect.

	Views		
	Top	Front	Right Side
Block A	____	______	__________
Block B	____	______	__________
Block C	____	______	__________
Block D	____	______	__________

A B C D

Fig. 3-7. Which block has been drawn correctly in the multiview?

If you can distinguish between these objects in their multiview projections, you are making real progress. Good luck.

DRAFTING ACTIVITY

1. Divide your plate into four sections.

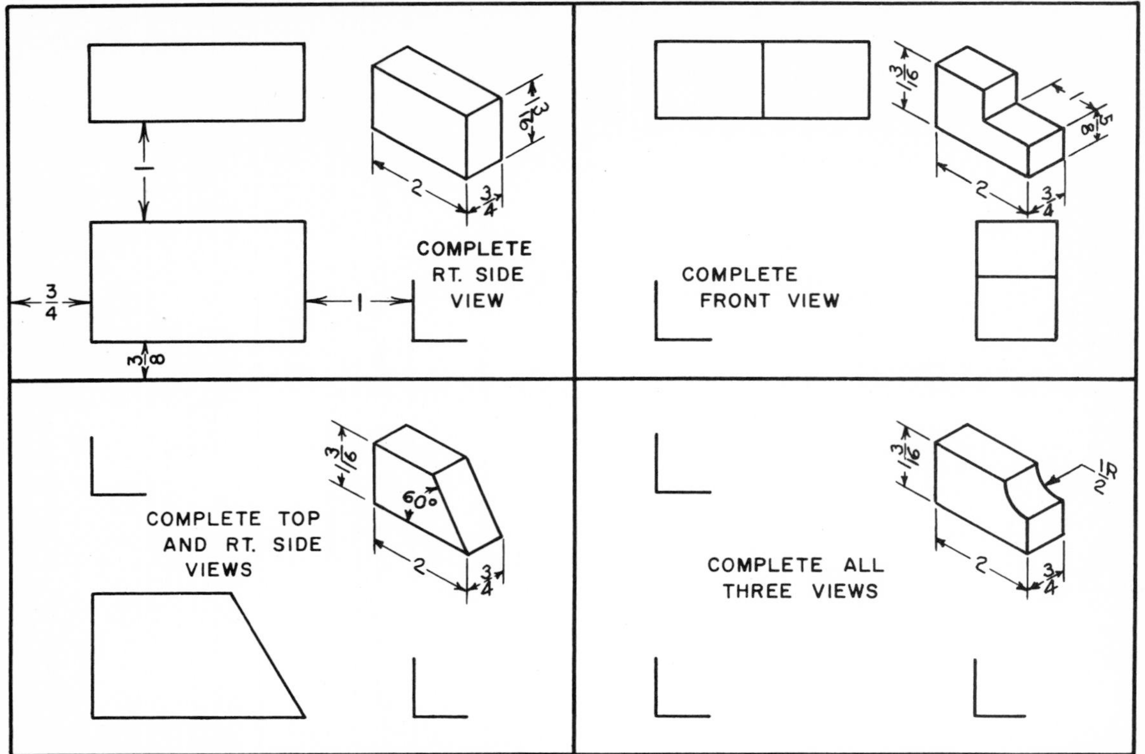

Fig. 3-8. Problems in multiview drawing.

2. First sketch, on another sheet of paper, the incomplete views; then you are to draw the views given and complete the views required in Fig. 3-8.
3. This is Plate No. 6. Number additional plates consecutively.
4. Sign your plate.

SELECTION OF VIEWS

The selection of views to represent an object is very important in drafting.

The draftsman is the one who must decide on the number of views to be drawn as well as the choice of views. In a three-view drawing, usually the top, front, and right-side views are drawn. In a two-view drawing the top and front views or the front and right-side views are drawn, depending on which ones best describe the object.

In selecting the views, give priority to the front view and consider the following suggestions:

1. Position the object so that the views will best describe its shape.

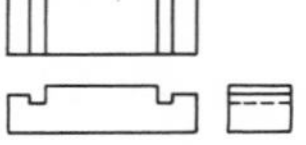

2. Position the object so that it is resting in its normal position.

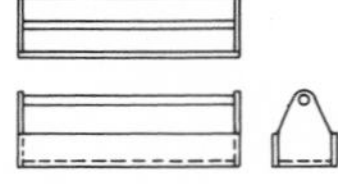

3. Position the object so that the least number of hidden lines will be required.

4. Position the object so that the arrangement of the views fits the plate, resulting in good balance and economical use of space.

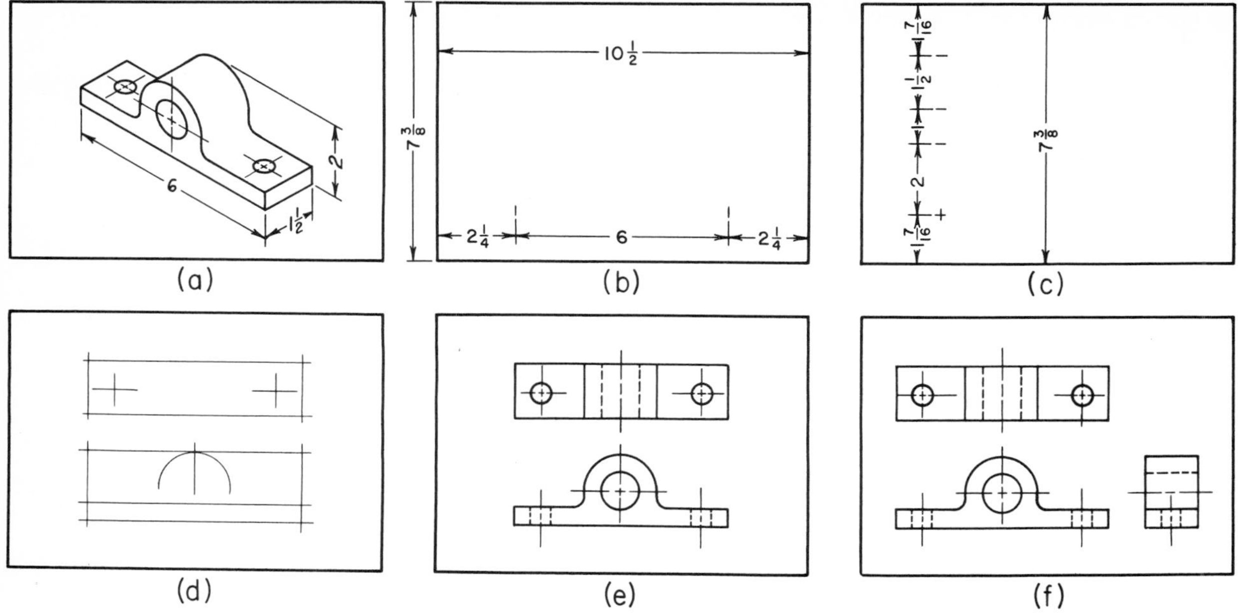

Fig. 3-9. Figuring the spacing for multiview drawings.

SPACING OF VIEWS

Before a working drawing is constructed, the spacing for the views must be figured. Let's see how this is done for a two-view drawing.

In Fig. 3-9a, a pictorial drawing of a bracket is shown. The working space of the plate is 10-1/2 in. wide by 7-3/8 in. high, Fig. 3-9b. To space the object horizontally, subtract the width of the object (6 in.) from the working-space (10-1/2 in.), and 4-1/2 in. remains (10-1/2 in.— 6 in. = 4-1/2 in.). Divide the 4-1/2 in. by 2 to get 2-1/4 in. for the spacing on each side of the object, Fig. 3-9b.

The vertical spacing is figured in a similar manner, but two views with spacing between these views are involved. Add the dimensions for the two views (2 + 1-1/2 in.) and the space between views (allowing at least 1 in., more space is necessary if several dimensions are to be placed between views). This totals 4-1/2 in. (2 in. + 1 in. + 1-1/2 in. = 4-1/2 in.). Subtract 4-1/2 in from the working space (7-3/8 in.) and 2-7/8 in remains. Divide this by 2 to get 1-7/16 in for the spacing at the top and bottom of the plate, Fig. 3-9c.

Block in views lightly with construction lines, Fig. 3-9d. When you are certain of your layout, darken arcs and circles first, and then darken all straight lines, Fig. 3-9e.

Spacing for a three-view drawing is figured in the same manner, except that spacing between the front and right side views must be provided, Fig. 3-9f.

Always figure your spacing on scrap paper before starting the layout of an object.

DRAFTING ACTIVITY

1. Use plain notebook paper to sketch three views of the pen holder base shown in Fig. 3-10.

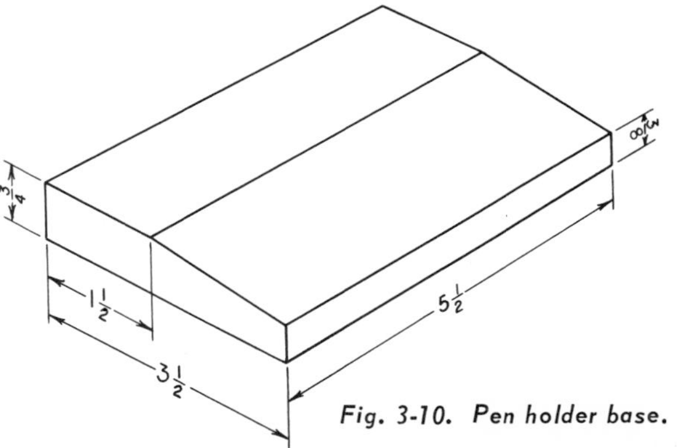

Fig. 3-10. Pen holder base.

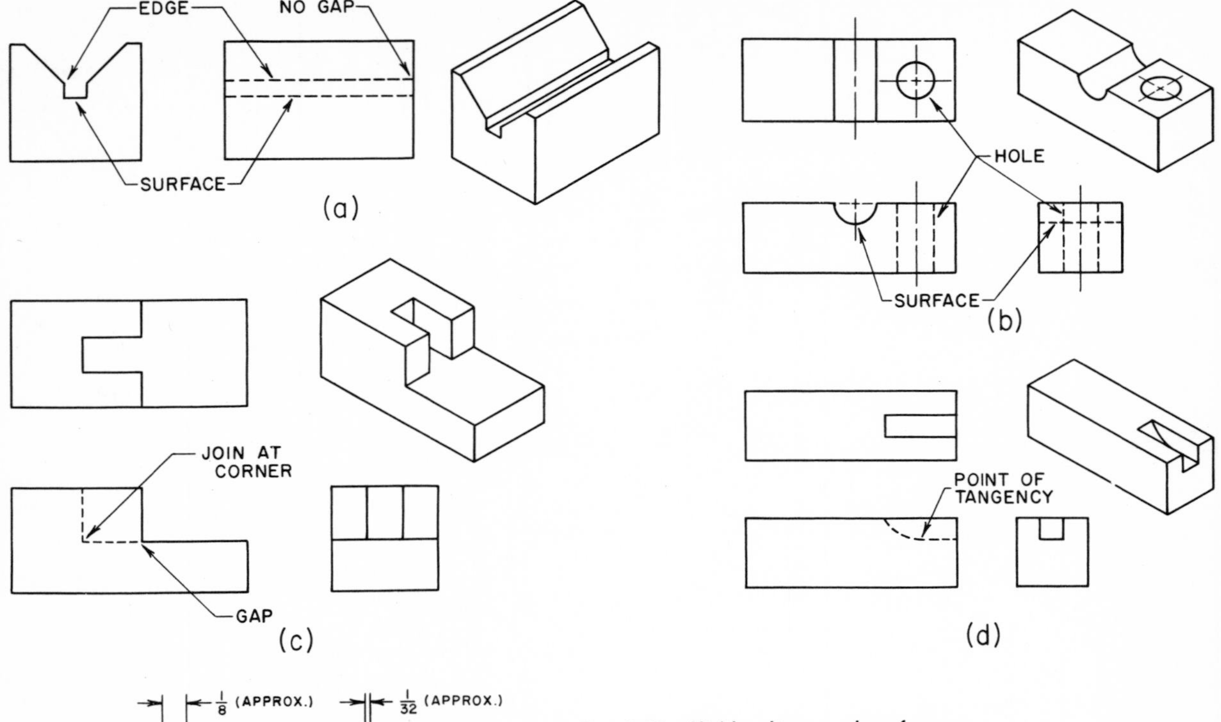

Fig. 3-11. Hidden lines and surfaces.

2. Select views carefully and follow the sketching technique studied in Unit 2.
3. Submit the sketch to your instructor for approval.

When your sketch of the pen holder base has been approved, you are ready to make a three-view drawing of it using instruments.

DRAFTING ACTIVITY

1. Lay out border and title blocks but do not divide into sections.
2. Make a three-view drawing of the pen holder base. Follow the suggestions in Fig. 3-9 for layout of the sheet and blocking in of the views.
3. Sign your plate.

HIDDEN LINES AND SURFACES

Edges, surfaces, and corners which are not visible in a particular view are shown by hidden lines in order to further clarify the drawing, Fig. 3-11. In this way the workman is able to "see" hidden edges and contours, and better visualize the object. Note the construction of the hidden line in Fig. 3-11e.

When drawing hidden lines observe the following rules:

1. Hidden lines start with a dash joining the object line, Fig. 3-11a, unless the hidden line is a continuation of an object line, then a gap is shown between object line and the first dash, Fig. 3-11c. This indicates clearly where the object line stops.
2. Dashes join at hidden corners, Fig. 3-11c.
3. Hidden arcs begin with a dash at the point of tangency, Fig. 3-11d.

Hidden lines are sometimes omitted by experienced draftsmen when the drawing seems to be clearer without them, but it will be well for you to include them unless otherwise directed by your instructor.

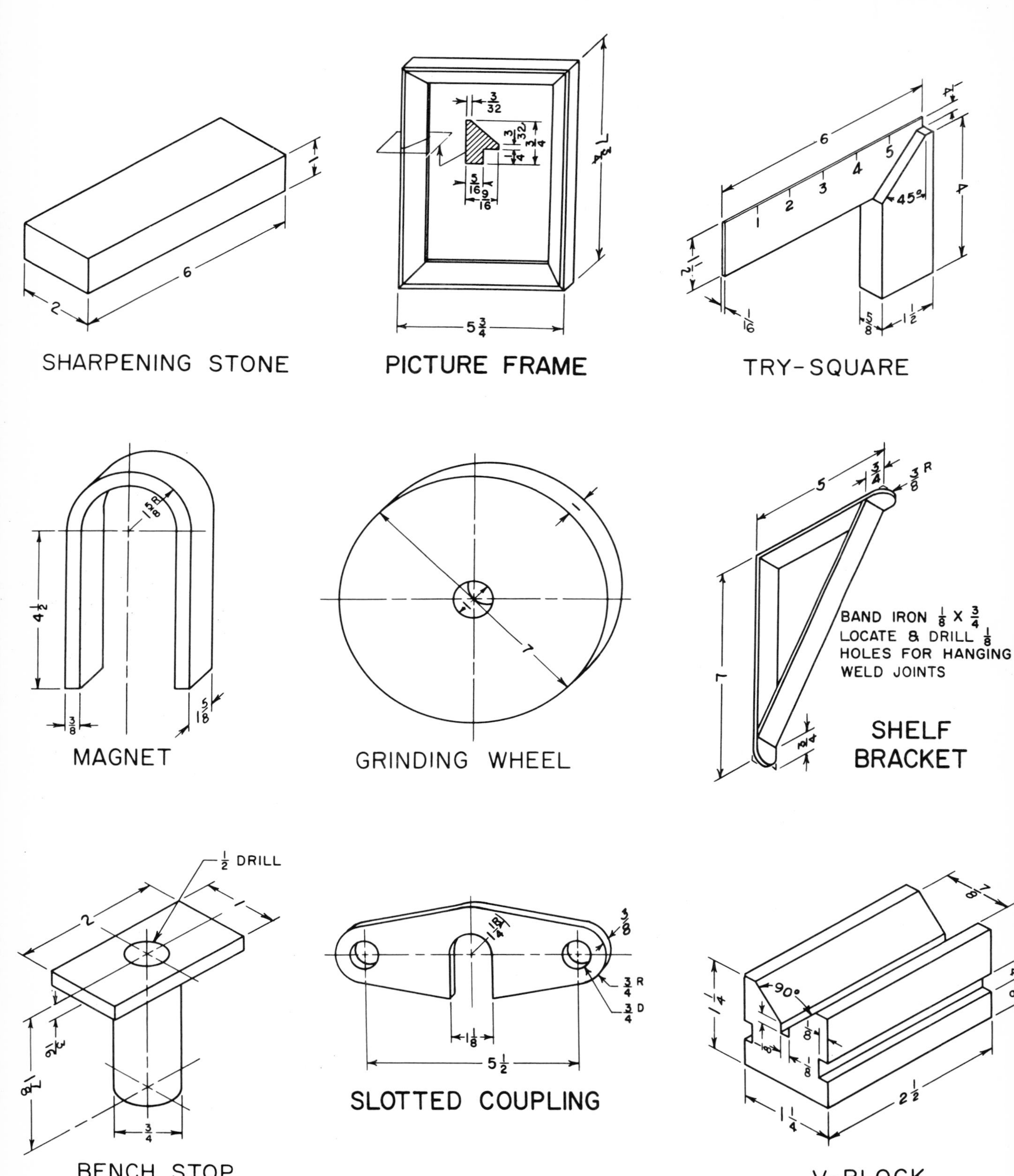

Fig. 3-12. Problems in multiview drawing. (Additional problems on pages 106, 107, 108.)

DRAFTING ACTIVITY

1. With your instructor's approval, select one or more of the objects in Fig. 3-12 and make a multiview drawing of each on a separate sheet of paper.
2. Draw the necessary views.
3. Show all visible and hidden lines.
4. Sign your plate.

IS DRAFTING IN YOUR FUTURE?

Does working with the T-square and triangles appeal to you? Have you the patience for accuracy and detail? Can you visualize three-dimensional objects readily? If you can answer "yes" to these questions, and if you have an interest in mechanical things, you may be interested in drafting or a related occupation as your life's work.

There are a number of occupations to which an interest in drafting relates. These can be classified as jobs in drafting, engineering, architecture, and industrial arts teaching. First, let's take a look at some jobs in drafting.

DRAFTING OCCUPATIONS

Jobs in drafting are usually grouped in five levels, depending on the type of work performed and skill required. The chief draftsman is the person who plans and directs the work of the drafting department. He reviews the jobs coming into the department and assigns them to persons having the necessary skills and knowledge to perform the jobs. Let's take, for example, an engineer's or inventor's idea for a product--perhaps an improved pencil sharpener. This idea would be given to a designer (a designer may work from his own ideas, too), who designs, sketches, and writes specifications for a workable product. To do this he must have a thorough understanding of drafting, as well as a knowledge of manufacturing processes and materials.

The designer may prepare the finished working drawings for the pencil sharpener, or his sketch and specifications may be given to a detailer who will prepare the drawings.

After the working drawings are prepared they are handed to a checker who checks them for errors. This is important work, for any errors remaining in a drawing could cost a company a great deal of money in loss of time and material.

When the drawings have been carefully checked, they are given to a tracer who prepares tracings so prints can be made. The job of the tracer is usually the beginning position. It also affords an excellent opportunity to increase one's knowledge of industrial drafting practices. In smaller industries one draftsman may do all of the work from designing to tracing.

All drafting positions require neatness, accuracy, normal vision, and considerable technical knowledge. Many industries require previous training in drafting which can be acquired in high school drafting courses. For high level drafting positions, further education in a vocational-technical school or college is desirable and in some types of work, essential. In some industries, beginning draftsmen may learn the work through a three or a four-year apprenticeship. Training in related subjects such as English, math, physical science, electricity, metalwork, woodwork, and other shop subjects is essential. Usually the more training you have had upon entrance, the faster your advancement, and the higher your progress in drafting.

There is considerable opportunity for draftsmen in industry at the present time, and industrial trends indicate the demand will continue. See Fig. 3-13. Well-lighted rooms and clean surroundings make for

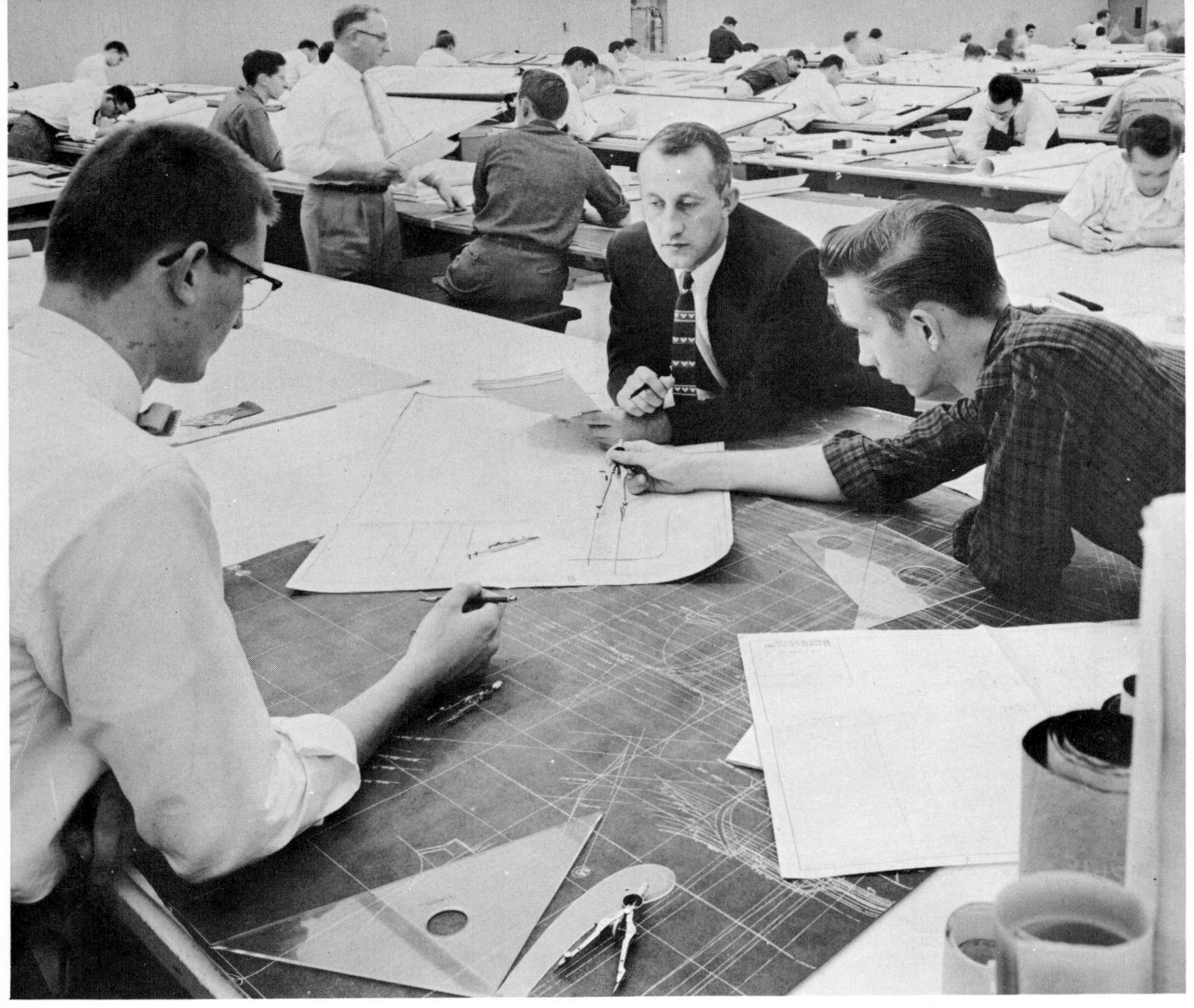

Fig. 3-13. A drafting department in industry (Chevrolet Div., General Motors Corp.)

desirable working conditions. The pay is good when compared with many other jobs in industry.

Long hours over the drawing board can be tiring and may cause eye strain. You will, however, have the satisfaction of drawing, and perhaps designing, many industrial products. Drafting is an occupation of a technical nature which can be entered without four years of college training.

If you have drafting ability; get along satisfactorily in math, science, and shopwork; are creative, accurate, and neat; you may want to investigate drafting as a career.

ENGINEERING

Engineers work with ideas and problems related to the transformation of materials into products useful to man. As a beginner he may do some drafting, but later on he will be developing ideas for new products or working out the mathematical and scientific solutions to problems which will be drawn by others.

Most professional engineering positions require from four to five years of college training. Success in a college program is dependent to a large extent upon your aptitude and ability in English, math, and science courses, as well as technical subjects in engineering. Training in drafting and shopwork, although limited, is usually included in the college program.

With an expanding industrial economy, the employment outlook for engineers is likely to continue to be good. Salaries are

among the highest paid in industry and the working conditions, like those for drafting, are pleasant.

If you have ability in drafting, math, and science and like working with creative ideas, you may want to carefully consider the possibilities of a career in engineering.

ARCHITECTURE

The architect designs buildings--houses, churches, schools, factories--and other structures with concern for construction, appearance, and function.

Like the engineer, his training usually consists of four to five years of college with emphasis on English, math, science, and technical courses. The architectural student ordinarily receives more training in drafting than the student engineer.

The opportunities for entering the field of architecture are favorable in view of our large residential and commercial building programs. The beginning architect usually starts as a junior draftsman and with experience moves to chief draftsman. Further work with an architectural firm leads to one of the specialized branches of construction supervision, specification writing, or designing of structures. About half of the architects in the United States achieve the goal of setting up their own businesses.

If you have ability in drafting, math, and science, are creative and like artistic work, you may want to study further the field of architecture.

INDUSTRIAL ARTS TEACHING

Teachers of industrial arts instruct junior and senior high students in one or more areas, such as: drafting, electricity, metal, wood, or crafts. Four to five years of college are required in the training of industrial arts teachers. Those interested in preparing for this field should have high aptitude and ability in drafting and shopwork, and a good background in English, math, and science.

The demand for teachers of industrial arts is high and is likely to continue.

Industrial arts teachers enjoy pleasant working conditions, creative work, and considerable freedom in planning their work.

If you do well in drafting and shop subjects, enjoy creating things, appreciate good craftsmanship and design, you may want to consider teaching industrial arts.

For additional information on these and other occupations related to drafting, talk to your industrial arts teacher or school counselor.

QUIZ - UNIT 3

1. What is a working drawing?
2. What is the meaning of orthographic projection?
3. How many views are needed to describe a football field? Why?
4. What shop projects can you name which require only one view?
5. What things should you consider in selecting the views of an object?
6. Hidden lines are used for what purposes on drawings?
7. Name the five types of drafting positions and describe the duties of each.
8. What are the requirements for entering the field of drafting?
9. Describe the work of the engineer and the qualifications for entering this field of work.
10. What is the work of the architect and how much training is required?
11. What is the nature of the work of the industrial arts teacher and what are the requirements for entering this field of work?

LETTERING AND DIMENSIONING

1. What kinds of lettering are used on drawings?
2. How are letters and numerals constructed?
3. How are drawings dimensioned?
4. What is simplified drafting?

All industrial drawings, with the possible exception of a hurried shop sketch, contain information which is lettered. The lettering and dimensioning on your plates will affect the appearance of your work just as much as your technique with instruments and sketching. In this unit you will want to begin to develop this skill so that you can start lettering and dimensioning your plates.

STYLE OF LETTERING

Two types of Gothic lettering are used --vertical and inclined, Fig. 4-1. The vertical letters are perpendicular to the

VERTICAL GOTHIC LETTERS

INCLINED GOTHIC LETTERS

Fig. 4-1. Gothic lettering.

line of lettering, as the name suggests, and the inclined letters are formed at a forward angle of 67-1/2 deg. The Gothic style refers to letters that are formed with single strokes of the pencil or pen rather than letters that vary in thickness, such as the Roman, Fig. 4-2. Gothic lettering can be done much more readily and is easier to read than other styles. For these reasons, it has become universally accepted as the style of lettering for all industrial drawings.

Fig. 4-2. Roman lettering. (Higgins Ink Co., Inc.)

In Fig. 4-3 are shown the vertical Gothic capitals (upper case), the small letters (lower case), and numerals as well as the strokes used in forming these. The inclined Gothic letters and numerals are shown in Fig. 4-4.

Both the vertical and inclined styles are used in industrial drawings; therefore, you should learn to use each style. Your instructor will help you decide which style to use with your beginning drawings.

Capital letters (caps) are used for title block information and for notes, Fig. 4-5a. Occasionally, capitals and lower case (lc) letters are used for notes, particularly on map drawings, Fig. 4-5b. You may use your 2H pencil for lettering, or you may want to get one with a softer lead, such as an F or HB.

SIZE OF LETTERS

The size of letters varies with the size of the drawing. In your work you will follow the suggested letter sizes for the title block. You should use 1/8 in. capitals for notes on drawings unless otherwise directed by your instructor. When lower case letters are used with capitals, the body of the lower case letter is two-thirds the height of the capital. A few lc letters are as tall as the caps, extending either above or below the lc guide lines, Fig. 4-6.

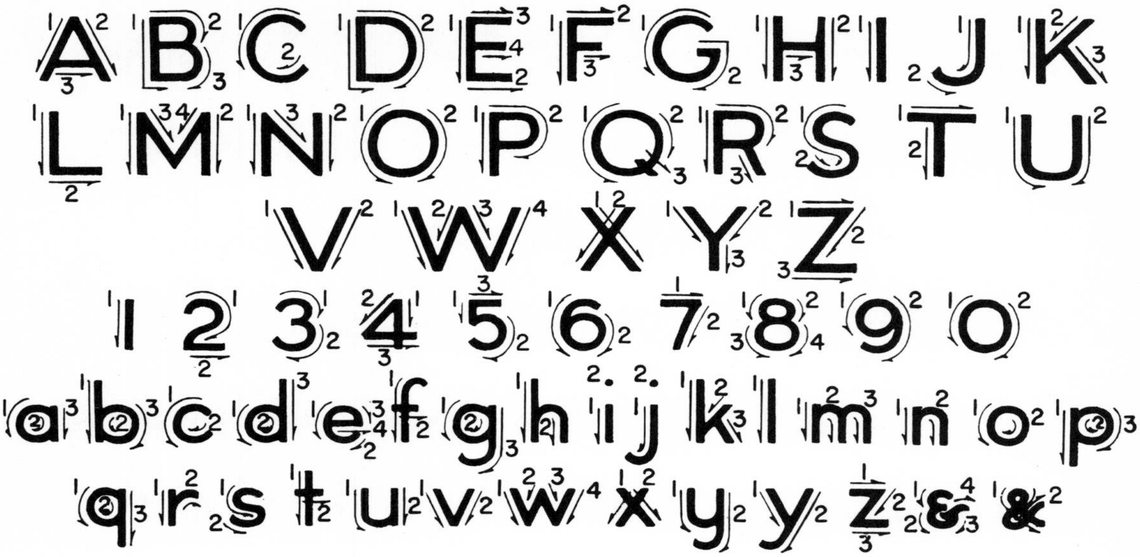

Fig. 4-3. Strokes and proportions, vertical Gothic lettering. (Higgins Ink Co., Inc.)

Fig. 4-4. Strokes and proportions, inclined Gothic lettering. (Higgins Ink Co., Inc.)

(a) $\frac{1}{4}$ DRILL 3 HOLES

(b) Boundary of property

Fig. 4-5. Notes on drawings.

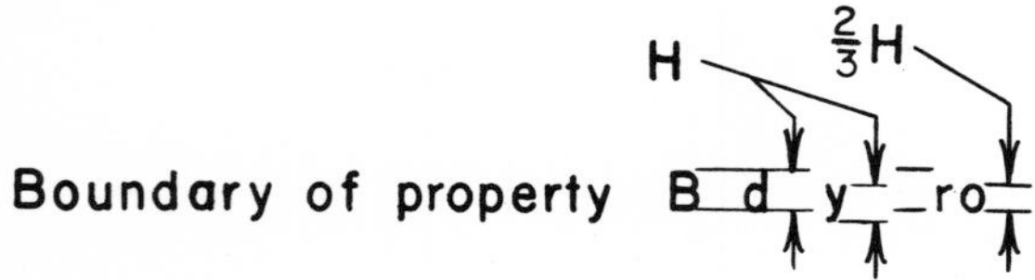

Fig. 4-6. Size of letters.

Numerals are equal in height (H) to capital letters, and fractions are twice the height of whole numbers, Fig. 4-7.

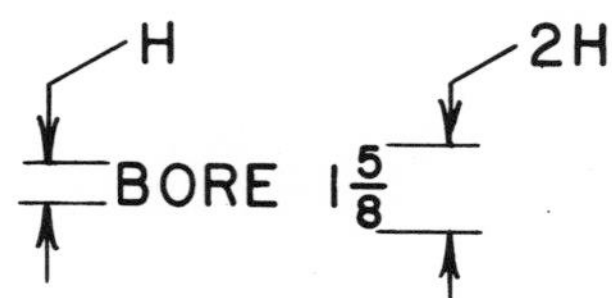

Fig. 4-7. Numerals and fractions.

The space between letters, words, and sentences is judged by the eye. You must exercise care in seeing that the spacing is compact but not crowded, Fig. 4-8.

GUIDE LINES

Horizontal guide lines assist in keeping your lettering in line and uniform in

One letter space ½H to H

GOOD LETTERING TECHNIQUE REQUIRES PRACTICE AND CON- CENTRATION. TRY TO IMPROVE EACH TIME YOU LETTER.

Two letter spaces H

Adjust space to letter size

Fig. 4-8. Spacing letters, words, and lines.

height. Use them for all lettering--one numeral or several lines of notes, Fig. 4-9.

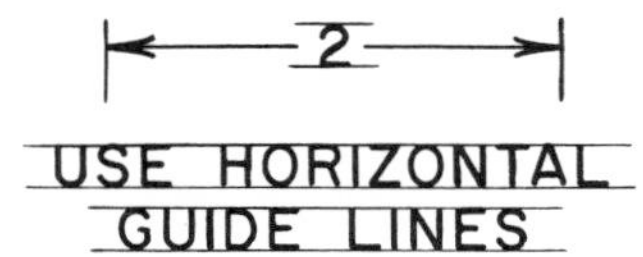

Fig. 4-9. Horizontal guide lines.

Vertical or inclined guide lines should be used as a guide to the correct slope of letters, Fig. 4-10.

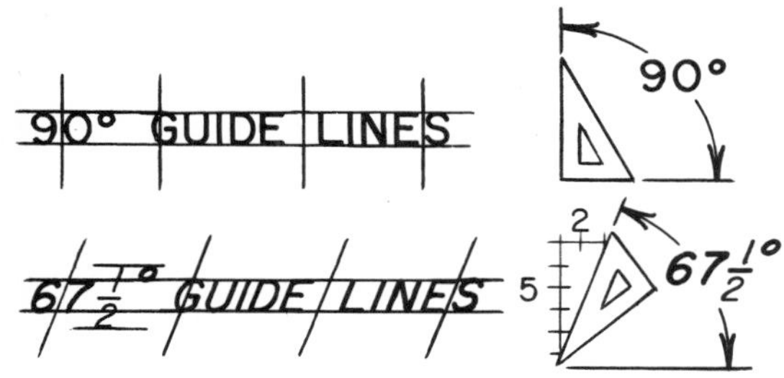

Fig. 4-10. Vertical and inclined guide lines.

Guide lines should be drawn lightly so that erasures are not required, and they should be invisible at an arm's length. Use a 4H pencil.

POSITION FOR LETTERING

Lettering should be done with the arm and hand supported on the drawing table or board. The pencil should be held with a relaxed grip as in writing. Place a sheet of paper or cloth under your hand and arm, to protect your drawing when lettering. Fig. 4-11.

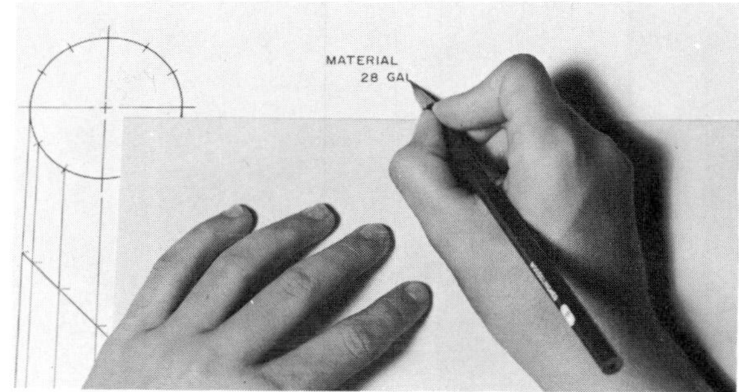

Fig. 4-11. Protect your work when lettering and dimensioning.

LETTERING SAMPLES

Samples of lettering carelessly done and samples properly lettered appear in Fig. 4-12.

Your skill in lettering can best be developed by:

1. Doing a short lettering exercise to acquaint you with the strokes necessary to form letters and numerals correctly.
2. Lettering your plates.
3. Practicing during your free time outside class.

DRAFTY SAYS: "Strive for neatness and accuracy in all drafting problems."

AIDS TO GOOD LETTERING

Instruments are available for use in lay-

POOR		GOOD
YOUR LETTERING	Spacing crowded	YOUR LETTERING
S P E A K S F O R	Spacing loose	SPEAKS FOR
YoUR DRAWING.	Height not uniform	YOUR DRAWING.
LET IT SPEAK	Incorrect slope	LET IT SPEAK
WELL. TAKE	Poorly formed letters	WELL. TAKE
PRidE IN All	Do not mix caps and lc	PRIDE IN ALL
THAT YOU DO.	Letters too heavy	THAT YOU DO.

Fig. 4-12. Your lettering affects the appearance of your work.

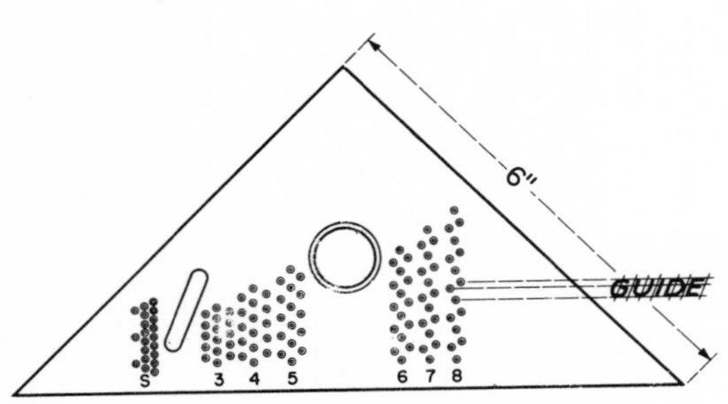

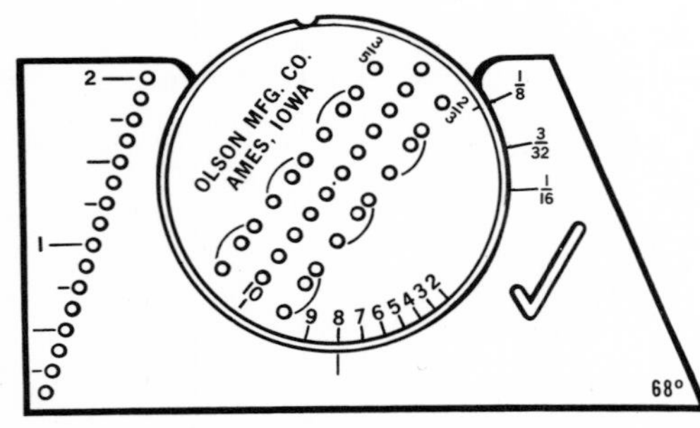

Fig. 4-13. Lettering instruments.
(Olson Mfg. Co. and Braddock Instrument Co.)

ing out guide lines for lettering, Fig. 4-13. Perhaps your instructor has one of these.

LETTERING DEVICES

Many professional draftsmen use lettering devices for lettering their drawings, particularly when the lettering is on sheets from which prints are to be made. Two such devices are shown in Fig. 4-14. However, far more drawings are lettered by freehand than are lettered with the use of instruments.

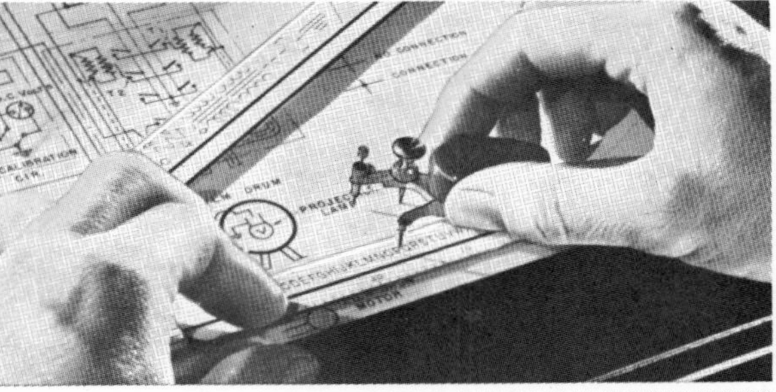

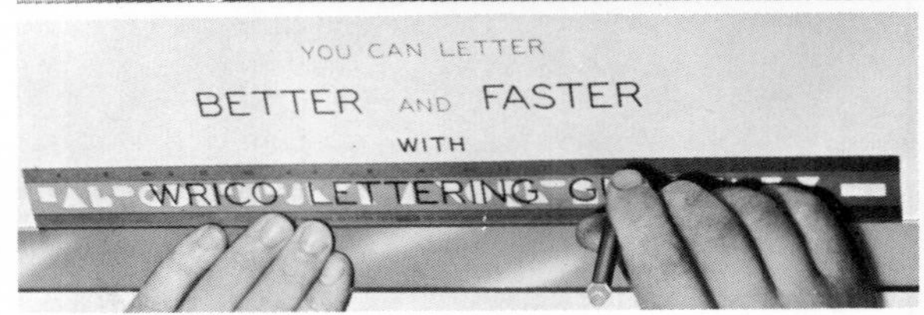

Fig. 4-14. Lettering devices. (Keuffel & Esser Co. and Wood-Ragan Instrument Co., Inc.)

DRAFTING ACTIVITY

1. Divide your plate into four sections.
2. Letter 1/8 in. alphabets and numerals in section A. Allow 1/8 in. between lines.
3. Use horizontal guide lines, and vertical or inclined guide lines.
4. Refer to your lettering charts, Figs. 4-3, and 4-4, when lettering.
5. Your instructor will tell you when the other sections are to be lettered.

DIMENSIONS AND SHOP NOTES

Drawings provide the craftsman with two essentials: shape description through the views, and size description through di-

mensioning. Notes furnish other information such as kind of material, finish, and quantity.

You are now familiar with the theory of shape description. Information regarding size description will be discussed here under dimensioning practices.

DIMENSIONING PRACTICES

Dimensions indicate size of objects and location of parts. Let's look at some dimensioning practices.

1. Dimensions are placed to be read either from the bottom of the sheet or from the bottom and right side.

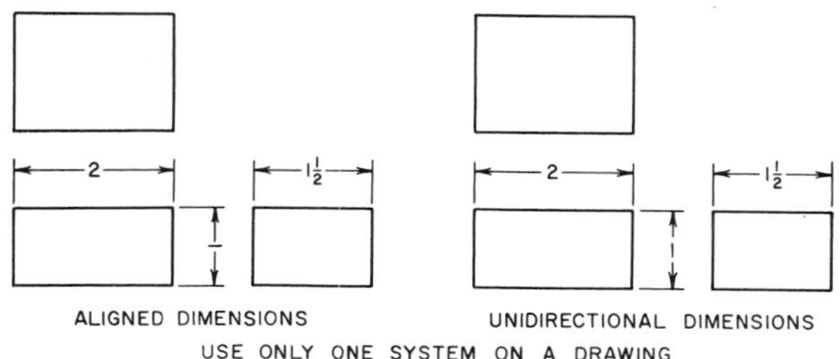

2. Dimensions on a simple drawing are placed between views. Exceptions may be made for purposes of clarity.

3. Dimensions are placed adjacent to view most descriptive of shape dimensioned.

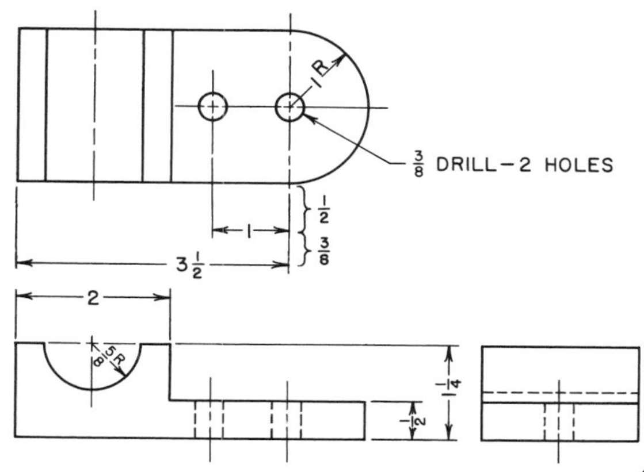

4. Dimension lines are spaced 1/2 in. from view; additional dimensions 3/8 in. apart (see illustration item 3). Never crowd dimensions.
5. Smaller dimensions are placed nearest the object. Over-all dimensions are always given for height, width, and depth (see illustration item 3).
6. Circles are dimensioned by giving the diameter in the rectangular view. Shop notes are directed to the circular view.

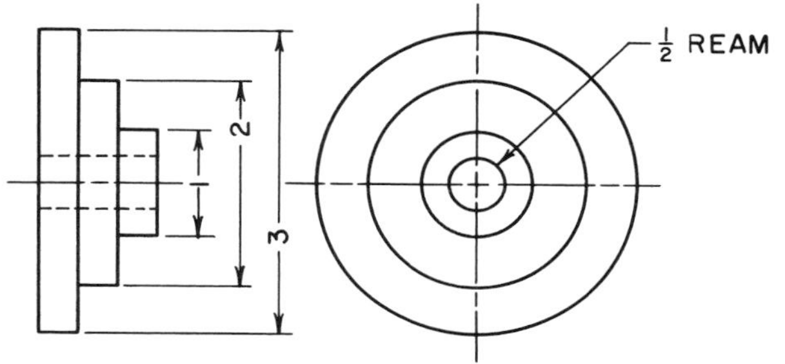

7. Dimensions are staggered for ease of reading (see illustration item 6).
8. Symbols for feet (') and inches ('') are used. When all dimensions are in inches, the inch marks should be omitted.

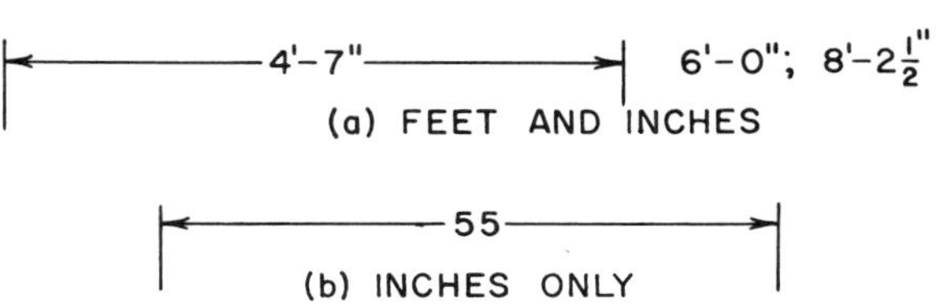

9. The radius (R) is used in dimensioning arcs. The "R," located above the dimension line, always follows the dimension (See illustration item 3).
10. Holes are located around a common center by dimensions and shop notes.

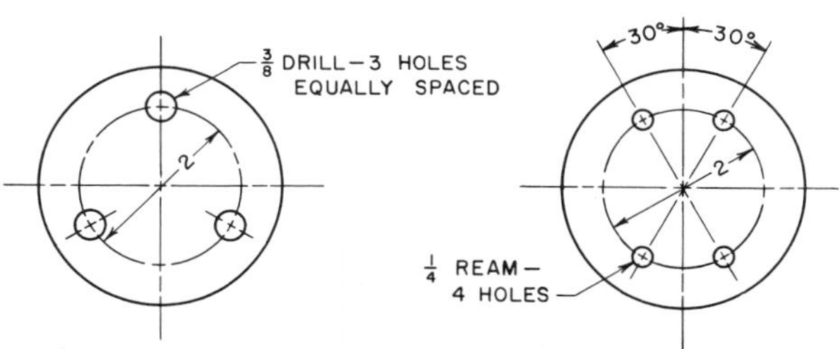

11. Angles are indicated by degrees, on an arc swung from the vertex, (a) and (b). For angles less than 90 deg., dimensions are placed horizontally, (a); for larger angles on the contour, (b). Some angles such as a chamfer require two dimensions, (c) and (d).

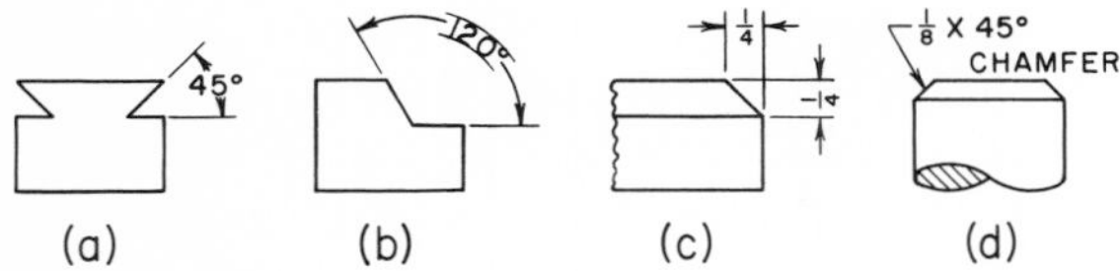

DIMENSIONING SMALL SPACES

Crowding dimensions into a small space produces poor drawings. Instead, try the methods shown in Fig. 4-15.

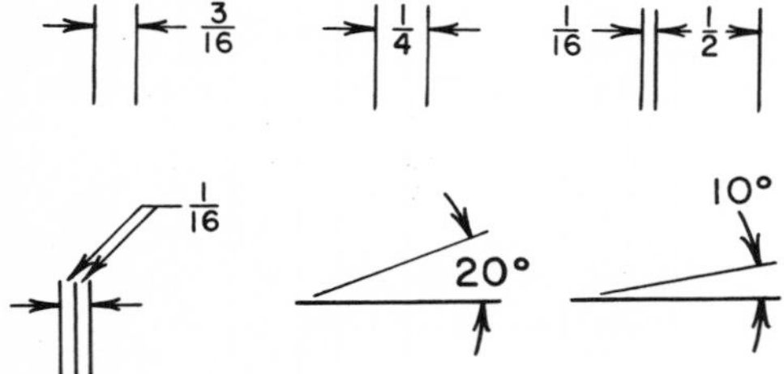

Fig. 4-15. Dimensioning small spaces.

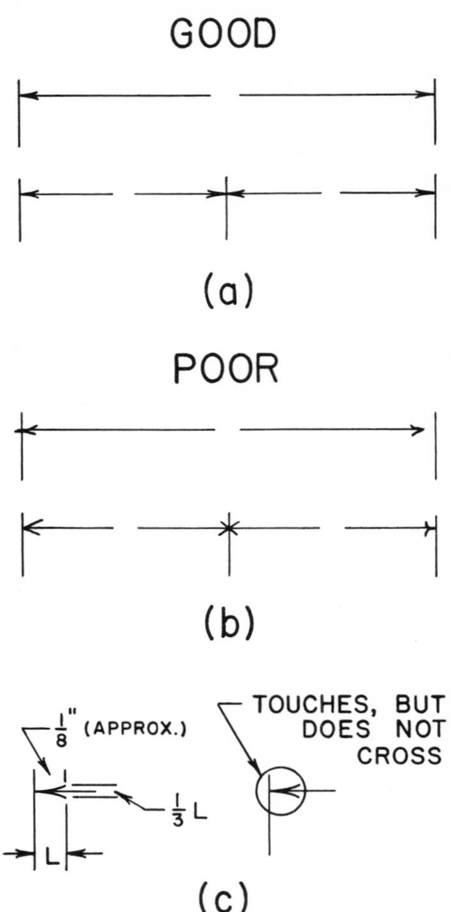

Fig. 4-16. Arrowheads.

ARROWHEADS

The draftsman should be as careful in forming his arrowheads as the Indians were in forming theirs. It's true that drafting arrowheads are not made to spear game, but they are designed to point to exact spots on the drawing. So it is important that they be "sharp" and well balanced, as shown in Fig. 4-16a. Draw each half of the arrowhead with your lettering pencil in one stroke toward or away from the point. The length is usually 1/8 in. and should be uniform on each drawing. Make the width about 1/3 of the length, Fig. 4-16c.

Take pride in the formation of arrowheads, letters, and numerals, and your efforts will be rewarded.

SIMPLIFIED DRAFTING

In some industries "simplified drafting" is being used. This is a term applied to drafting procedures in which "shortcuts" are taken and yet accuracy is still maintained in the work. Examples of simplified drafting practices would be: the substitution of dots for arrowheads, Fig. 4-17a; the drawing of only one view of an object and indicating the thickness or diameter, Fig. 4-17b; the use of freehand sketches in place of instrument drawings; and the use of abbreviations and symbols on drawings. Machine screw threads of 1 in. in diameter or less are usually drawn as conventional symbols or in simplified form rather than in their true shape, Fig.

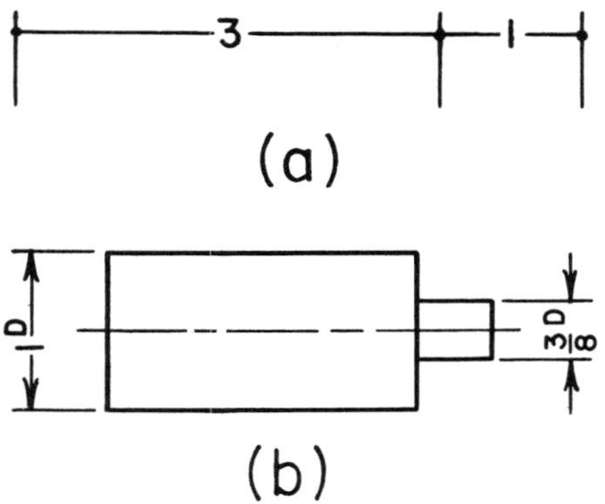

Fig. 4-17. Simplified drafting.

4-18. Simplified drafting practices may differ in each industry using the system.

Because the standard system is used in most industries as well as in schools, you should first study this system. Once you understand this system you will then be in a position to judge when simplified drafting can be used most effectively.

DRAFTING ACTIVITY

1. Study the alphabet of lines, page 104 as it pertains to dimension lines, extension lines, and leaders.
2. Dimension and letter the working drawings which you completed earlier.

QUIZ - UNIT 4

1. Why is the Gothic style of lettering used on industrial drawings?
2. What are the two styles of Gothic lettering?
3. When should you use capital letters? Lower case letters?
4. How high should capital letters be on your plates? Lower case letters? Numerals and fractions?
5. How much space is placed between words? Between sentences?
6. When should horizontal guide lines be used? Vertical or inclined guide lines? What weight should they be drawn?
7. How may you protect your drawing when you are lettering or dimensioning?
8. What information is supplied by shop notes?
9. How large should arrowheads be drawn?
10. Tell what is meant by simplified drafting and give some examples.

NEW WORDS FOR YOU TO USE

1. Dimension (di-men'shun).
2. Gothic (Goth'ik).
3. Simplified (sim'pli-fied).
4. Staggered (stag'er-ed)

Fig. 4-18. Conventional and simplified representation of machine threads.

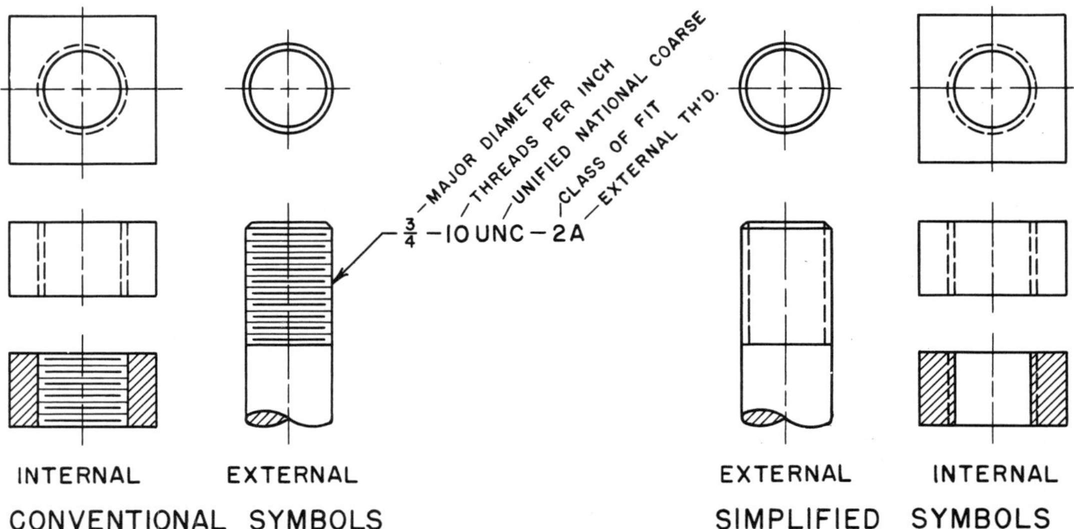

AUXILIARY AND SECTIONAL VIEWS

1. What are auxiliary views?
2. What are sectional views?
3. How are these used in drafting?

In addition to the regular views in a working drawing, it is sometimes necessary to draw some "special" views of an object, to show more clearly certain features. Two of these special views are <u>auxiliary views</u> and <u>sectional views</u>.

Auxiliary views are used in obtaining the true size and shape of inclined surfaces such as the one shown in Fig. 5-1.

Sectional views show the object as if a part of the object were removed and you could view its internal shape, Fig. 5-2.

Both of these views are quite helpful to the workman. You will want to know how they are drawn.

AUXILIARY VIEWS

Suppose you had to lay out on a piece of sheet metal the true size and shape of the inclined surface in Fig. 5-1a. A true representation of this surface does not appear in any of the three views. However, an auxiliary view can be projected which would be a true representation. Let's see how it is developed.

1. The inclined surface is viewed from a position perpendicular to the surface, Fig. 5-1b.
2. Usually, not more than two regular views are needed to project the auxiliary view; the view in which the inclined surface appears as a line (front view, Fig. 5-1a) and one other view, such as the top view.
3. Construction lines (very light) are projected perpendicular from the inclined surface, Fig. 5-1c.
4. The reference (back-edge) line AB is drawn parallel to the inclined surface, Fig. 5-1d.
5. The dividers are used in transferring widths from the top view, Fig. 5-1e. Care is taken not to punch holes in the drawing with the divider points.
6. Lines are drawn to complete the auxiliary view in Fig. 5-1f. Actually, more than the inclined surface is visible from the auxiliary plane, but usually only the inclined surface is shown.

Auxiliary views can be projected from any view in which the inclined surface appears as a line. In the preceding problem the projection was made from the front view and, therefore, is known as a front auxiliary. A projection from the top view would be called a top auxiliary and from the right side, a right side auxiliary.

You will find your knowledge of auxiliary views very helpful when you are working with the unit on sheet metal drafting.

DRAFTY SAYS: "Don't forget to clean your T-square and triangle occasionally with art gum and soft cloth."

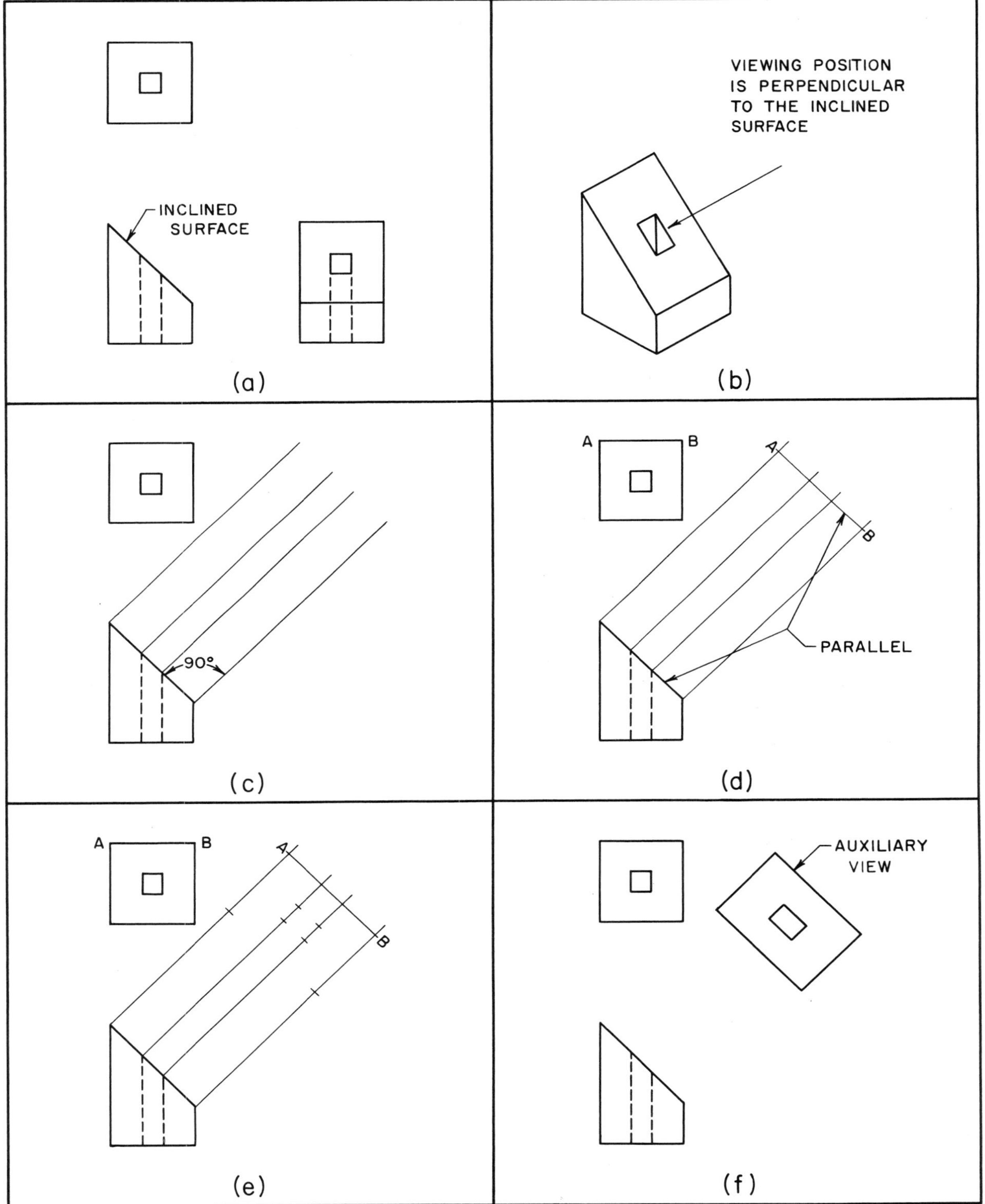

Fig. 5-1. Drawing an auxiliary view.

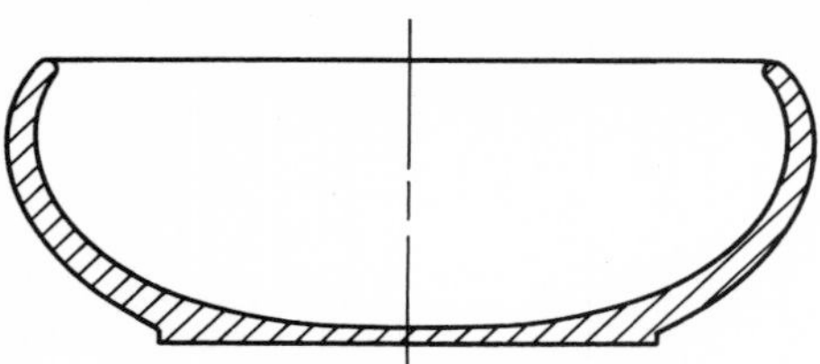

Fig. 5-2. Sectional view of a bowl.

Fig. 5-4. Sectional view of a car engine. (Ford Motor Co.)

DRAFTING ACTIVITY

1. With your instructor's approval, select one of the problems in Fig. 5-3.
2. Draw two views and an auxiliary view.

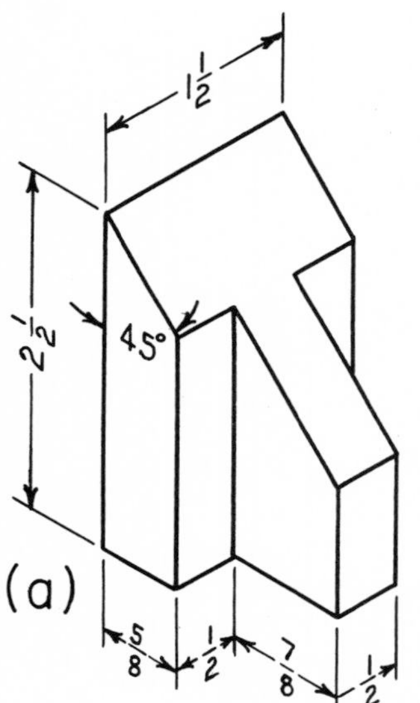

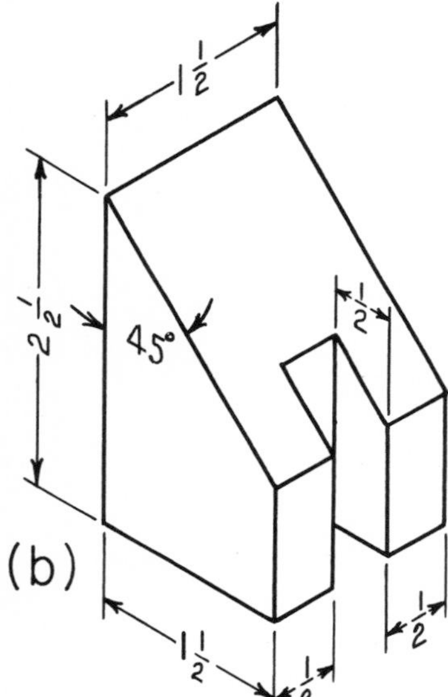

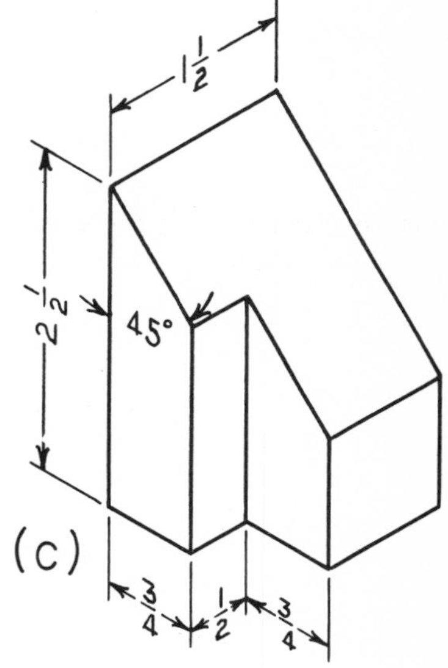

Fig. 5-3. Auxiliary problems.

SECTIONAL VIEWS

Several of the major automobile manufacturers have exhibited, throughout the country, engine and chassis assemblies of their cars. Perhaps you have seen one of these exhibits and noticed the cutaway sections of carburetors, gear-mechanisms, and cylinder blocks, Fig. 5-4. The sections have been removed to show the operation of the various parts.

The purpose of the sectional views in drawing is to show more clearly the shape and operation of complex objects. Let's see how the full section and the half section are constructed.

First, imagine a cutting plane has cut the object in half, Fig. 5-5a. Next, imagine that the front half has been removed, Fig. 5-5b. What you would be viewing is a full section since our cutting plane has passed all the way through the object. The section lines have been drawn to further clarify the interior shape of the object at the

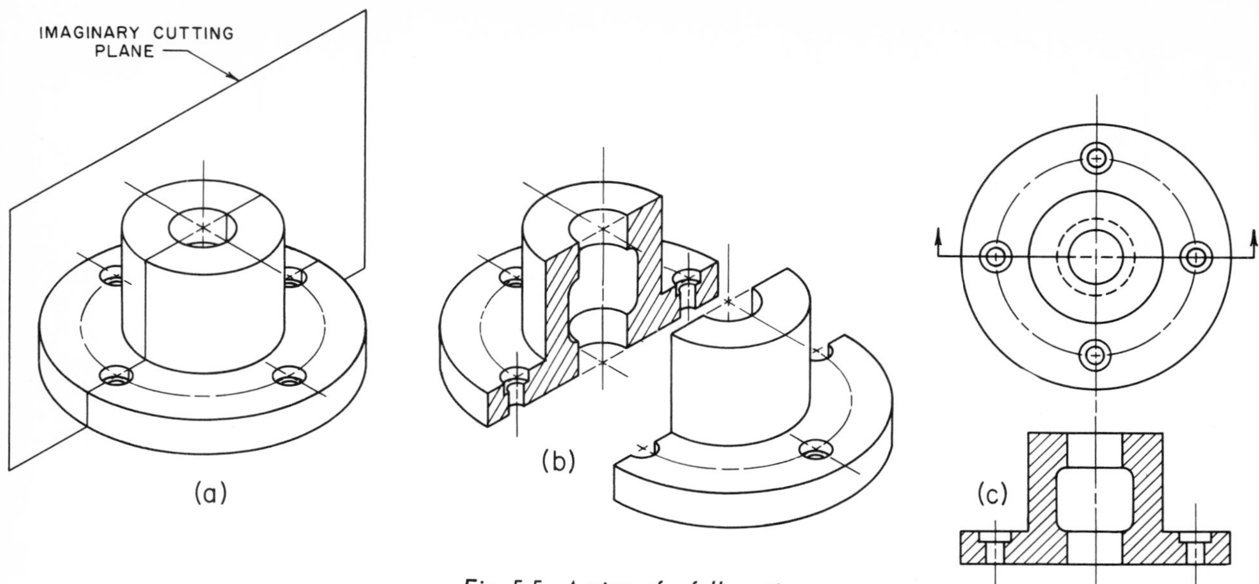

Fig. 5-5. A view of a full section.

cutting plane. Notice the cutting plane line in the top view of Fig. 5-5c. The arrows indicate the direction of sight.

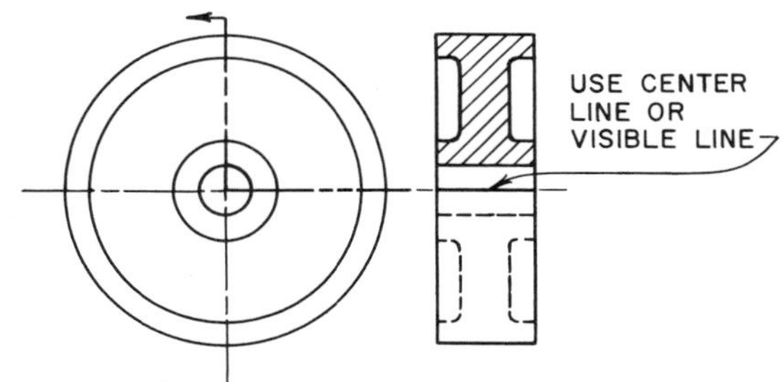

Fig. 5-6. Half section.

Fig. 5-7. Other types of sections.

A half section would be a view in which the cutting plane passes only half way through an object and one quarter of the object is removed, Fig. 5-6. Other types of sectional views are shown in Fig. 5-7.

SECTION LINES

Section lines are usually drawn at an angle of 45 deg. with a sharp 2H pencil, Fig. 5-5c. Draw the lines dark and thin to contrast with the heavier object lines. Space the lines by eye about 1/16 in. apart (on small drawings about 1/32 in.; large drawings, 1/8 in.). The spacing of section lines should be uniform.

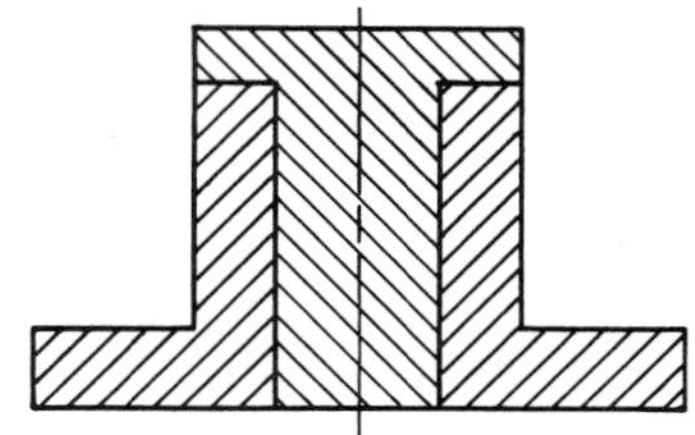

Fig. 5-9. Sectioning of adjacent parts.

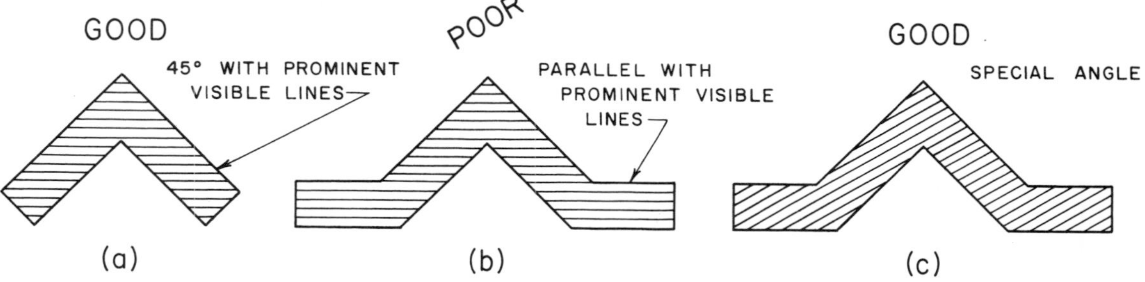

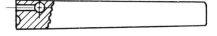

Fig. 5-8. Angle of section lines.

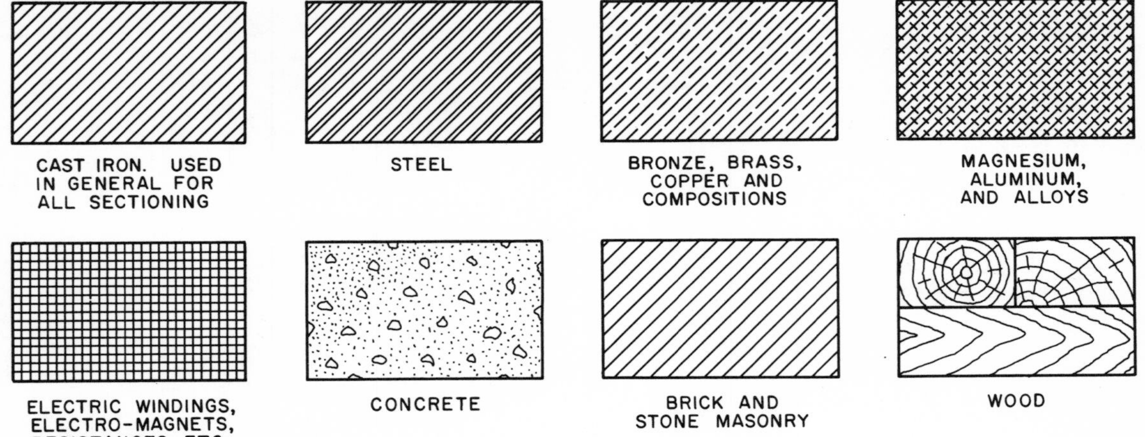

Fig. 5-10. Symbols for materials in section. (ASA Y 14. 2-1957-Line Conventions, Sectioning and Lettering).

The shape and position of the object sometimes require that section lines be drawn at a special angle, for example 30 deg., to prevent the section lines from being drawn parallel or perpendicular (or nearly so) to a prominent visible line bounding the sectional area, Fig. 5-8. Section lines change direction for adjacent parts, Fig. 5-9. Center lines are drawn in sectional views, but hidden lines are omitted unless they are needed for clarity.

The section lines shown in these sectional views are those used to indicate cast iron. However, when the section lines are not being used as a symbol to indicate type of material, this type of sectioning is commonly used for other materials. See Fig. 5-10 for specific representation of other materials in section.

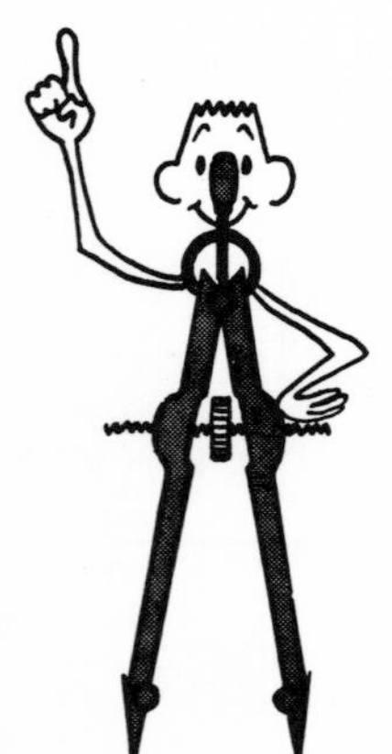

DRAFTY SAYS: "Be sure to sketch drafting problem on scrap paper first."

DRAFTING ACTIVITY

1. With your instructor's approval, select one or more of the problems in Fig. 5-11, page 52.
2. Draw two views, one representing a full section.
3. Dimension the drawing.

QUIZ - UNIT 5

1. The auxiliary view is projected from what view? Why?
2. How many views are needed in projecting an auxiliary view?
3. When would you use an auxiliary view?
4. What is a right side auxiliary view?
5. Sectioning of an object is used for what two purposes?
6. How does a full section differ from a half section?
7. Section lines are usually drawn at an angle of 45 deg. When would it be necessary to draw them at an angle other than 45 deg.?
8. When would you use the cast iron section lining to represent materials other than cast iron?

NEW WORDS FOR YOU TO USE

1. Auxiliary (og-zil'ya-ri)
2. Section (sek'shun)

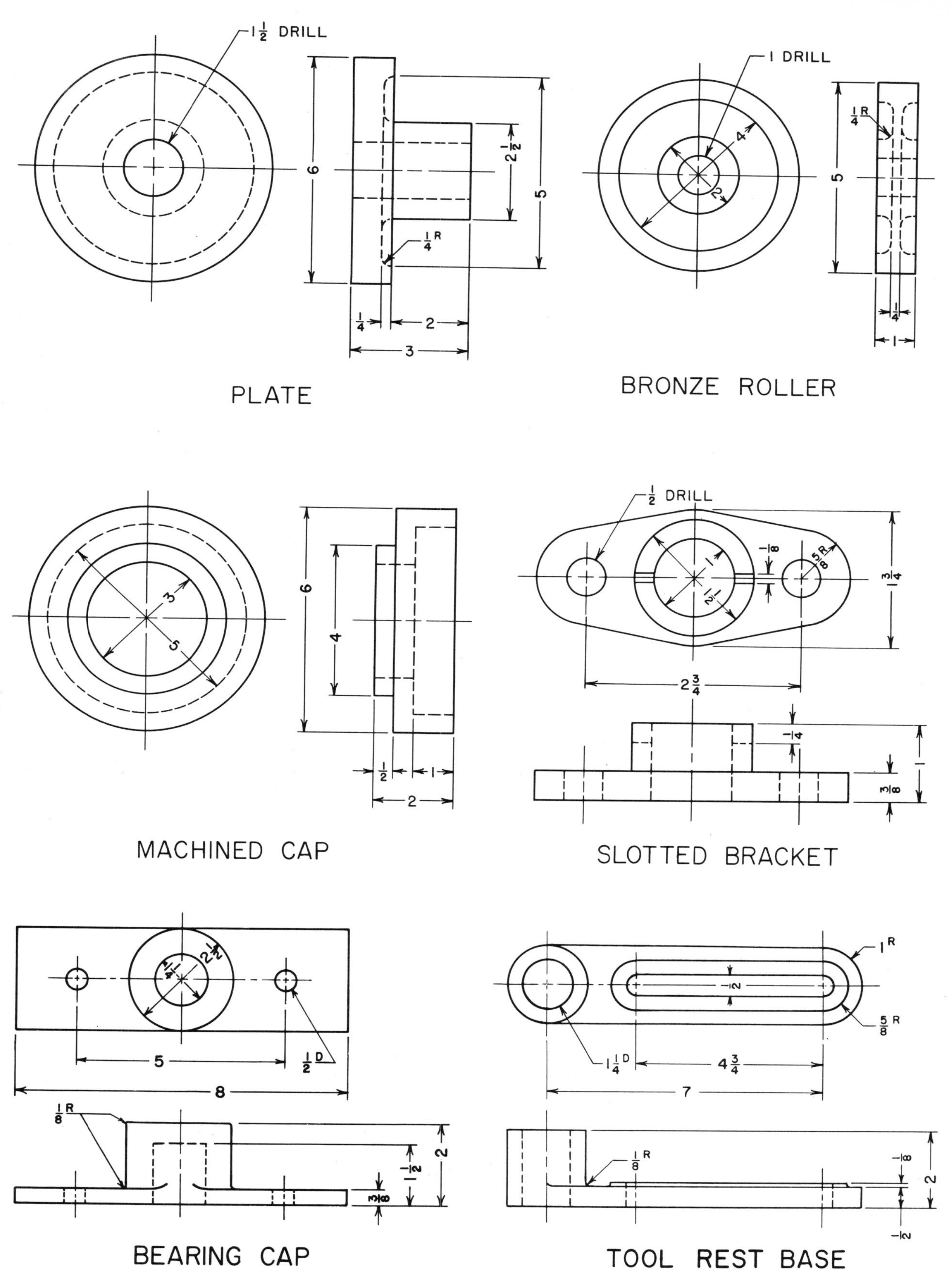

Fig. 5-11. Sectioning problems.

DRAWING TO SCALE

1. What does drawing to scale mean?

2. What different types of scales are used in drafting?

3. How are scale measurements made?

You have already learned to use the full-size scale in drawing an object full size. In drafting it is often necessary to make the drawing of an object smaller than its actual size. You have probably seen blueprints for a house. These had to be reduced considerably in size in order to get it on a reasonable size sheet of paper. Sometimes it is necessary for the draftsman to enlarge the drawing of a small screw or machine part in order to show the details clearly.

The secret to this reduction or enlargement of drawings is in the draftsmen's scale; it is all worked out for him--if he knows how to use it!

TYPES OF SCALES

There are three scales in common use today: those designed for the architect, the civil engineer, and the mechanical engineer. The architect's scale has a full-size scale of 12 in. marked off into sixteenths. You have been using this full-size scale. The architect's scale also has a number of other scales for reducing or enlarging drawings. These additional scales are divided into inches or fractions of an inch which represent feet. These scales are used in plans for building construction and for all objects dimensioned in feet and inches.

The civil engineer's scale, Fig. 6-1, is similar to the architect's scale, except the graduations are divided into decimal parts of an inch; usually 10, 20, 30, 40, 50, and 60 parts to an inch. This scale is useful in the drawing of aircraft and automotive machine parts where the decimal system has largely replaced the fractional system of dimensioning. It is also used in map drafting.

Fig. 6-1. Triangular civil engineer's scale.

The mechanical engineer's scale is laid out so that the major end unit represents 1 inch rather than a foot.

Sometimes, scales from each of these three basic types are used to form a combination scale.

If you learn to read one type of scale, you can also read other scales with a little help on the numbering system. Let's have a look at the architect's scale.

MEASURING WITH THE ARCHITECT'S SCALE

Four commonly used scales are:

Full-size or, 12" = 1' - 0"

Half-size or, 6" = 1' - 0"

Quarter-size or, 3" = 1' - 0"

Eighth-size or, 1-1/2" = 1' - 0"

The first of these (full-size) you have been using. If you want to draw an object half its actual size, you simply let 1/2 in. on the full-size scale represent 1 in. On the half-size scale a distance of 3-1/2 in. would be measured as shown in Fig. 6-2.

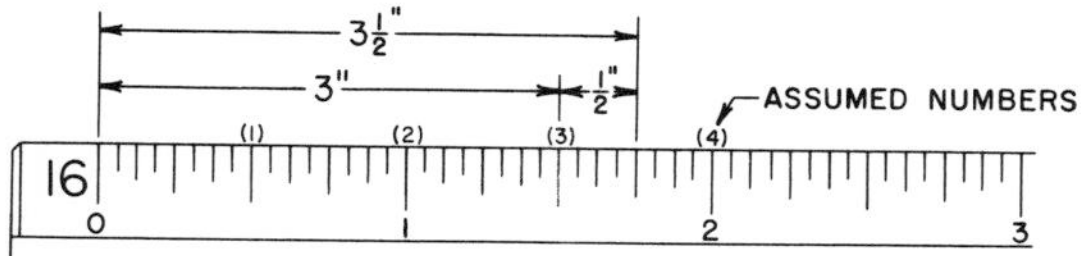

Fig. 6-2. Half-size, using the full-size scale.

Reading the half-size scale is easy when you let each half-inch represent one inch. The quarter-size mark now becomes a half-inch mark, the eighth-inch now becomes a quarter, and so on with the sixteenth mark becoming an eighth. Let's see how well you can use this scale.

DRAFTING ACTIVITY

1. Measure the length of the lines in Fig. 6-3.
2. Note that the scale is indicated as half-size.
3. Record your readings on a sheet of paper.

For objects to be drawn quarter-size, use the scale with the "3" marked on the end. In this scale the fine graduations 0 to 12 represent 1 ft. - 0 in. (or 12 in.), and you read the scale directly. A distance of 3-1/2 in. would be measured to the right of zero, Fig. 6-4.

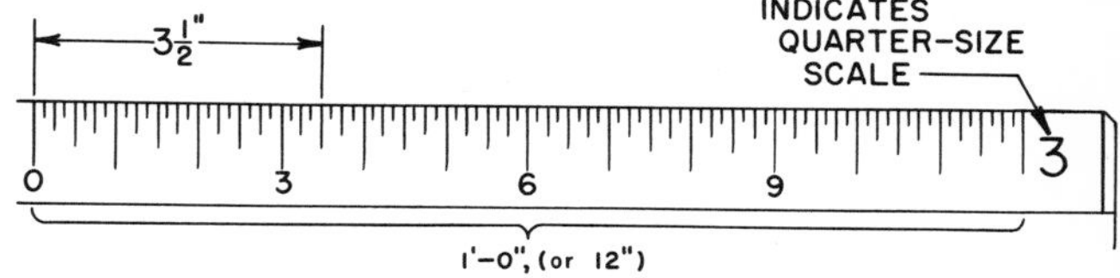

Fig. 6-4. Quarter-size scale.

To measure a distance of 1 ft. - 6-1/4 in., move your eyes to the left of zero to the 1 ft. mark, and this represents one point of your distance. Move your eyes to the right of zero until you come to 6 in. and to 1/4 in.; this represents the other point of your distance, Fig. 6-5.

Try your skill at measuring the lines assigned in the activity below.

DRAFTING ACTIVITY

1. Measure the length of the lines in Fig. 6-6.
2. Record your readings on a sheet of paper.

Drawing an object to eighth-size is done in the same manner as the quarter-size, only the scale marked "1-1/2" is

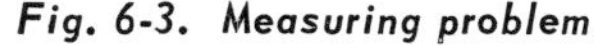

Fig. 6-3. Measuring problem.

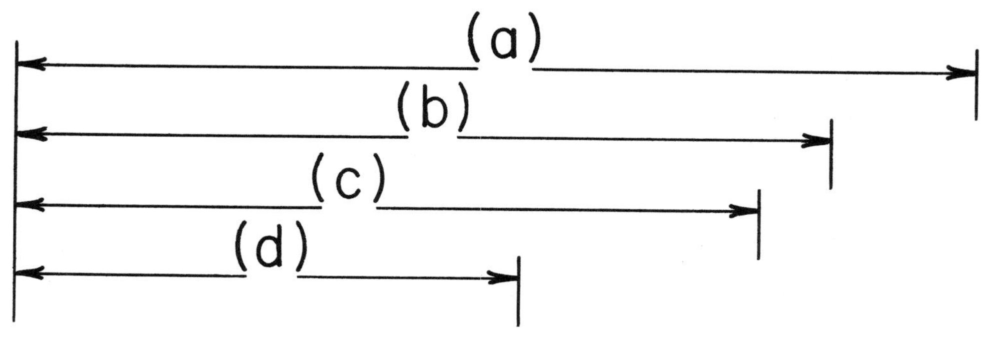

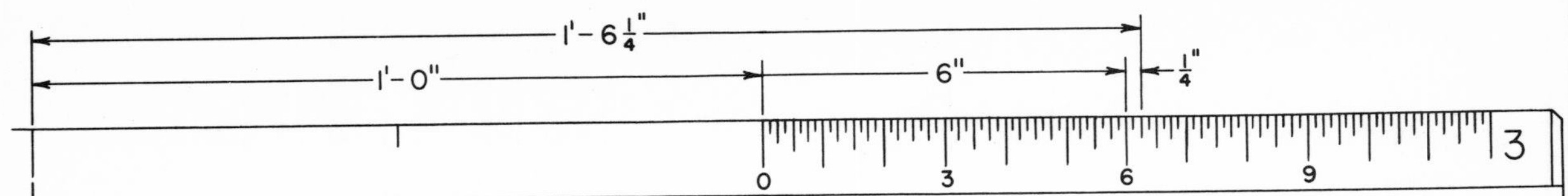

Fig. 6-5. Feet and inches on quarter-size scale.

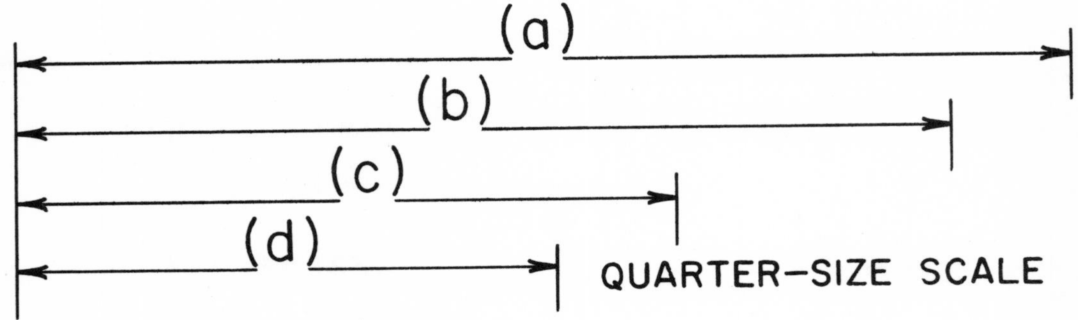

Fig. 6-6. Measuring problem.

used and is found on the opposite end of the scale from the quarter-size scale.

Sometimes there is a need to enlarge certain parts of an object in order to clarify some detail. The scales marked with the "1-1/2" and the "3" can be used to enlarge or to reduce a drawing. When the drawing of an object is to be enlarged, one and one-half its actual size, the fine graduated section from 0 to 12 on the scale marked "1-1/2" now represents 1 in. (instead of 1 ft.), Fig. 6-7.

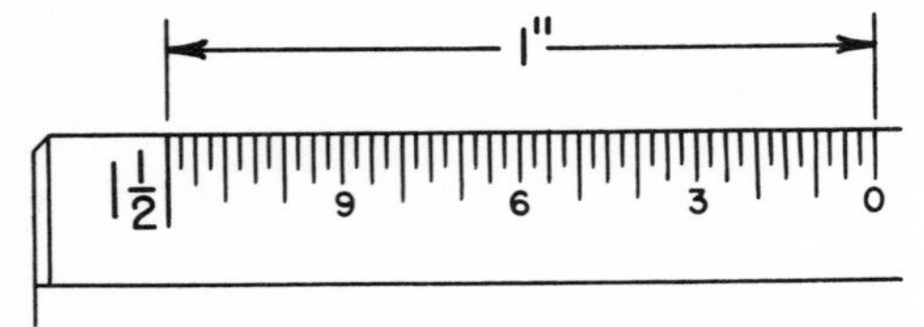

Fig. 6-7. Enlarging with the one and one-half scale.

The full-size scale can also be used to enlarge by letting 2 in. on the scale represent 1 in. on the object.

DRAFTING ACTIVITY

Measure and dimension the splined joint in Fig. 6-8.

Fig. 6-8. Measuring problem.

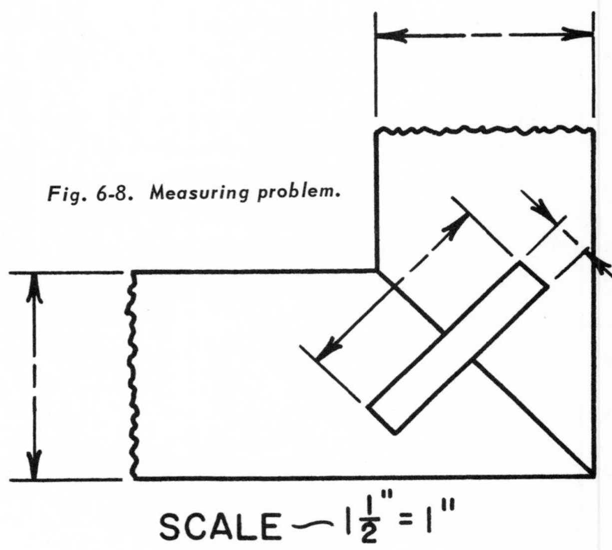

Other scales on the architect's scale are: 1 in., 3/4 in., 1/2 in., 3/8 in., 1/4 in., 3/16 in., 1/8 in., and 3/32 in. These scales represent feet on a scaled drawing. For example, the scale marked 1/4 means 1/4 in. on the drawing represents 1 ft. - 0 in. on the actual size of the object. It would be indicated on the drawing like this:

SCALE — 1/4" = 1'-0"

This is the scale most frequently used in drawing house plans:

FLOOR PLAN
$\frac{1}{4}'' = 1'-0''$

If your parents have the blueprints for the house in which you live, check the scale on these.

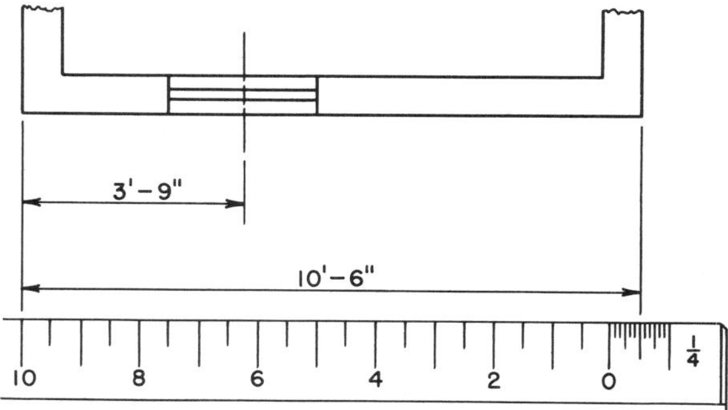

Fig. 6-9. Measuring with the one-quarter scale.

Note the difference between the one-quarter scale and the quarter-size scale:

One-quarter scale: 1/4 in.=1 ft. - 0 in. and is 1/48 actual size

Quarter-size scale: 3 in. = 1 ft. - 0 in. and is 1/4 actual size

In Fig. 6-9 note how the scale is used to measure, or to lay off a distance.

The scale is truly a valuable device to you in making a drawing. You can enlarge a drawing two or three times, or let 1 in. on the scale represent 50 to 100 miles or more in drawing a map.

DRAFTING ACTIVITY

1. Measure the distances marked in Fig. 6-10.
2. Note the scale for each line.
3. Record your reading on a sheet of paper.

TIPS ON MEASURING

1. Keep the scale clean.
2. Eye the scale directly from above.
3. Use a sharp pencil.
4. Use the largest scale that will fit the paper.
5. Do not move the scale to make individual measurements when laying off

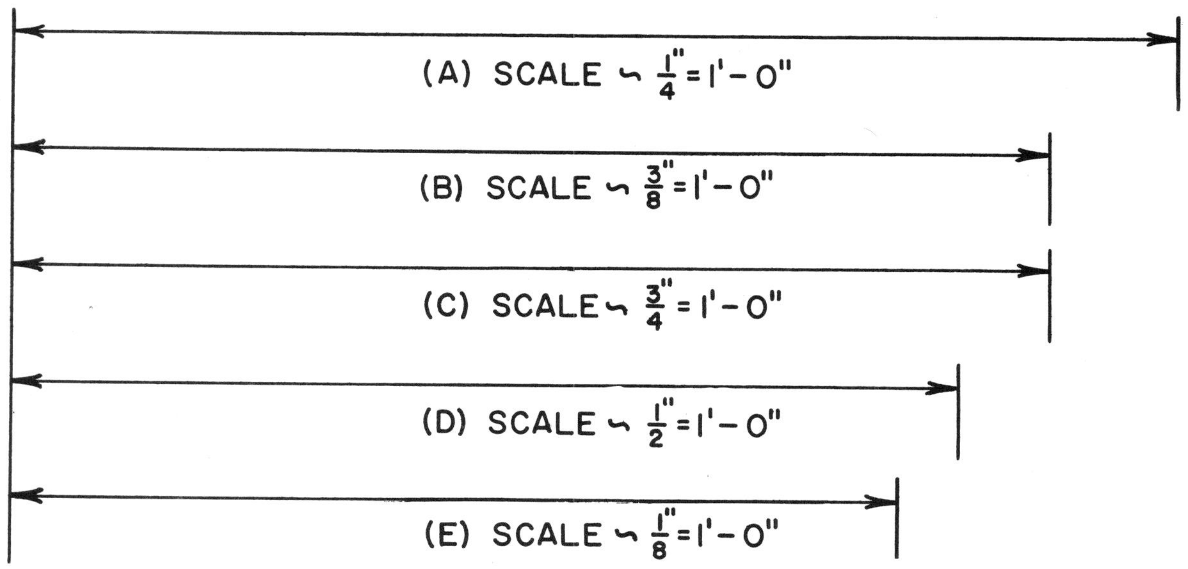

Fig. 6-10. Measuring problem.

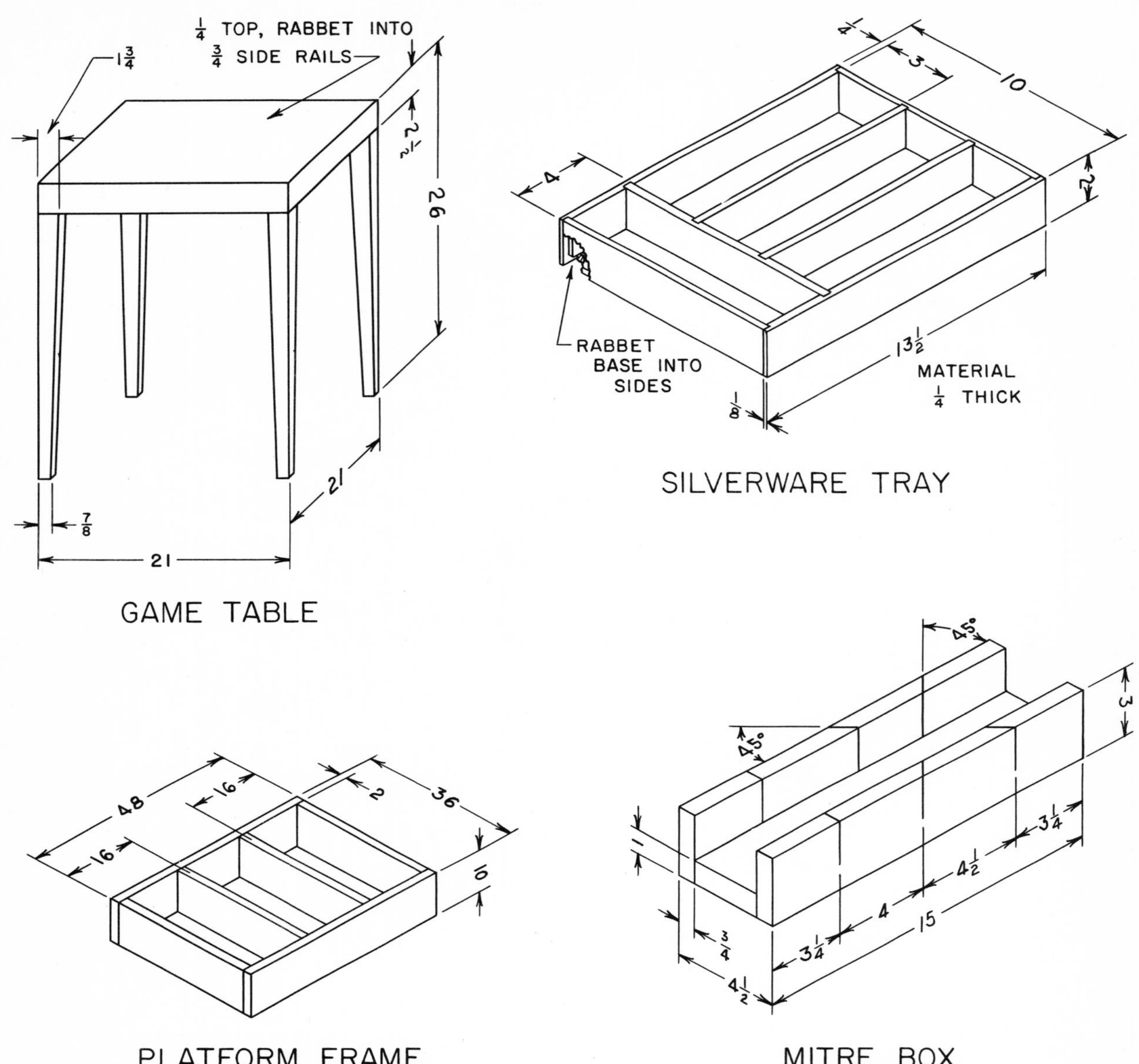

Fig. 6-11. Problems for scale drawing.

a series of distances along a line.

6. Recheck measurements after laying off.

You should be able to measure distances with any of the scales quite easily now.

HOW TO CHECK YOUR DRAWING

Do you know that a few minutes spent in checking your drawing may result in a higher grade? Particularly is this true when you spot and correct errors and omissions! Use the following list in checking your drawing:

1. Are there missing lines such as a short-object line, hidden line, center line, or dimension line?
2. Are there missing circles or arcs?
3. Are construction lines too heavy?
4. Are corners sharp and free from overlaps?
5. Have all necessary dimensions been provided?

Aerial view of freeway interchange. Highway expansion provides employment for many engineering and technical draftsmen. (California Div. of Highways)

6. Are letters, numerals, and arrowheads properly formed?
7. Have all shop notes been included?
8. Is the title block complete?
9. Are all lines of the correct weight?
10. Is your plate clean and neat?

DRAFTY SAYS: "Check your drawing carefully before handing it to your instructor."

DRAFTING ACTIVITY

1. From the problems in Fig. 6-11, make scaled multiview drawings as assigned by your instructor.
2. Problems are to be dimensioned.
3. Check your drawings by the ten-point check system.

QUIZ - UNIT 6

1. What does drawing to scale mean?
2. What scales are commonly used in drafting today? How do they differ?
3. When should an object be drawn to a size smaller than actual size?
4. When should an object be drawn larger than actual size?
5. How many different scales are on the scale (instrument) you are using?

PICTORIAL DRAWINGS

1. What are pictorial drawings?
2. How are pictorial drawings constructed?
3. When should an isometric view be drawn, and when would an oblique view be more satisfactory?

You have been getting some experience with working drawings which you should find useful in your shop work. There is another kind of drawing you will want to be able to do, and that is pictorial drawing. You constructed multiview drawings from pictorial drawings in Unit 3.

Pictorial drawings show several faces of an object in one view and are frequently used to supplement working drawings. Multiview drawings are best for showing details of construction, and for dimensioning purposes, but pictorial views are better for showing an object as it appears when you look at it.

There are two types of pictorial drawings which are commonly used in shop drawings--isometric and oblique. You will have an opportunity to learn how to draw these two types, and to learn something about a third type called perspective drawing.

ISOMETRIC DRAWING

Isometric drawing is a type of pictorial drawing that is used in making many shop drawings. It shows the object in one view rather than in several views.

Iso- is a prefix meaning equal and metric means measure, hence isometric means equal measure. It means the object is positioned (revolved and tilted) so that the measurement in all three directions (height, width, and depth) are made with the same scale, Fig. 7-1. The dark lines in Fig. 7-1 and all lines parallel to these lines are known as isometric lines. Horizontal lines in multiview drawings become

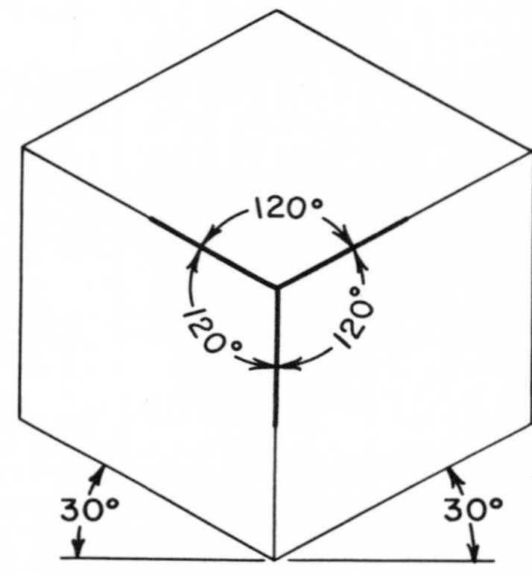

Fig. 7-1. Isometric axes.

30 deg. lines in the isometric view, Fig. 7-2.

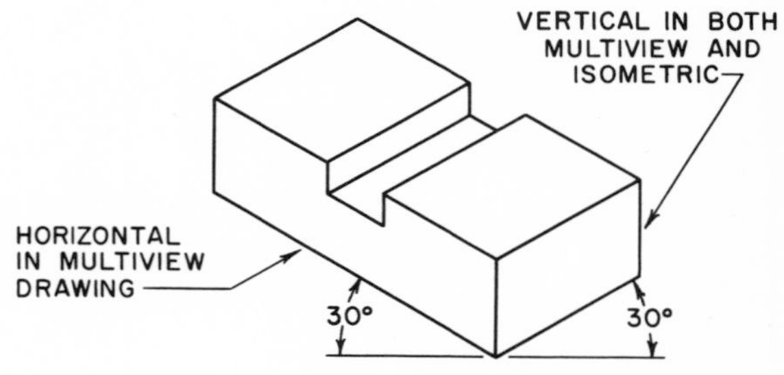

Fig. 7-2. Horizontal and vertical lines in isometric.

Vertical lines in multiviews remain vertical in the isometric view, Fig. 7-2. Let's see how an isometric drawing of the

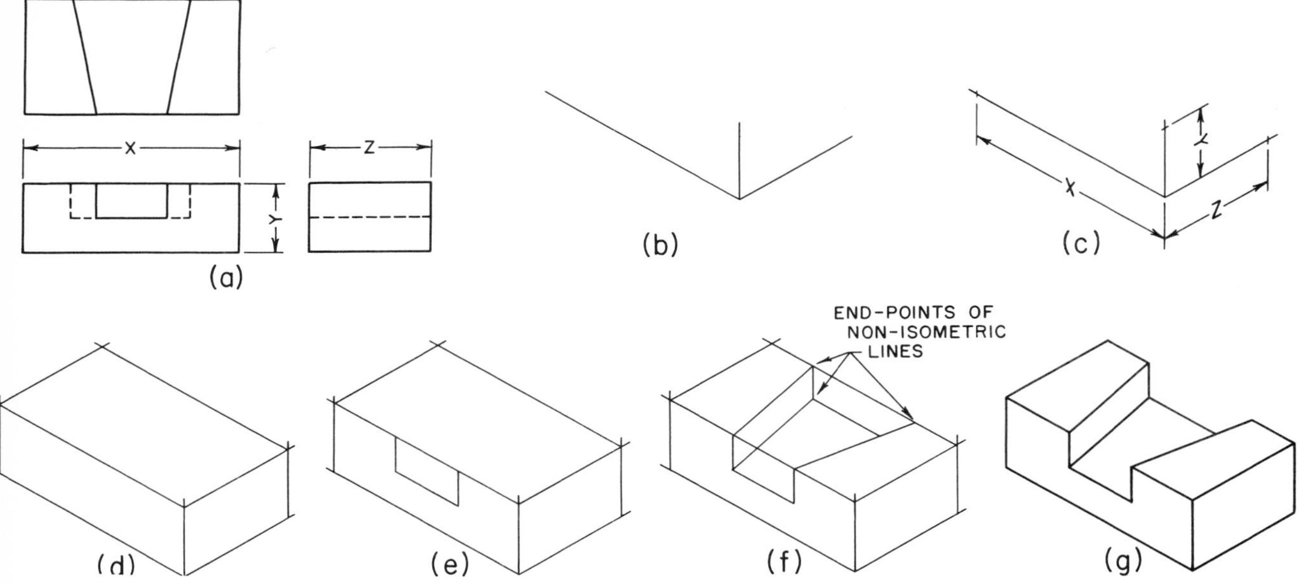

Fig. 7-3. Steps in constructing an isometric drawing.

slotted block, Fig. 7-3a, is constructed.

Procedure for constructing an isometric drawing:

1. Select the position of the object which will best describe its shape.
2. Start by laying out the axes for the lower corner, Fig. 7-3b.
3. Make over-all measurements in their true length on the isometric axes or lines parallel to the axes. Fig. 7-3c.
4. Construct a "box" to enclose the object, Fig. 7-3d.
5. Draw isometric lines of the object, Fig. 7-3e.

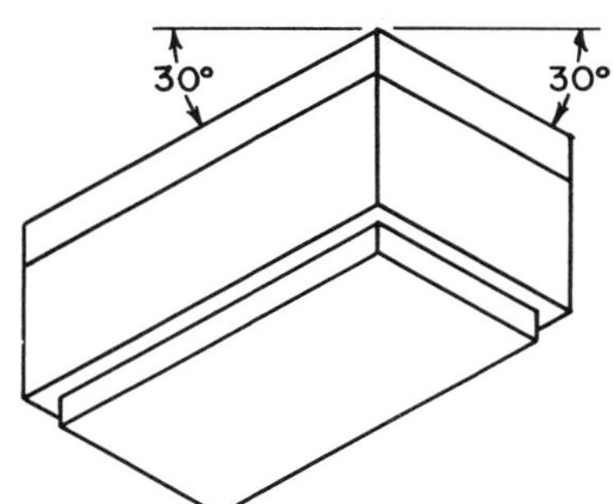

Fig. 7-4. Isometric drawing viewed from below the object.

6. Draw non-isometric lines (lines which are neither horizontal nor vertical in the multiview projection) by first locating the end points of these lines and then connecting the points by use of a straightedge, Fig. 7-3f.
7. Do not show hidden lines in isometric drawings; they are used only when clarity demands it.

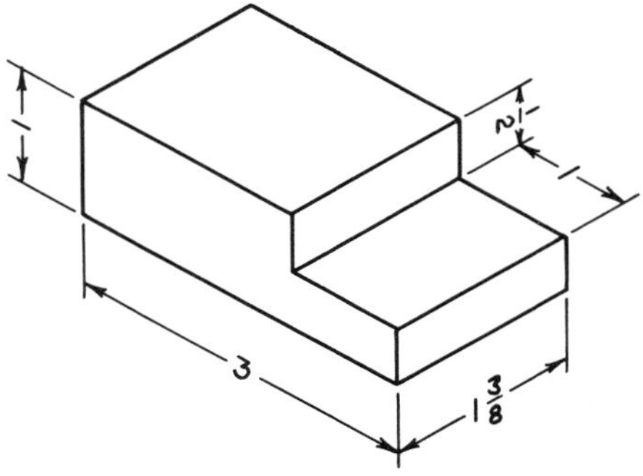

Fig. 7-5. Isometric dimensioning.

8. Darken all object lines to complete the isometric drawing, Fig. 7-3g.

Isometric views may also be drawn as viewed from below the object. The isometric axes are then projected 30 deg. below horizontal as shown in Fig. 7-4.

DIMENSIONING ISOMETRIC DRAWINGS

Dimension lines are parallel to the

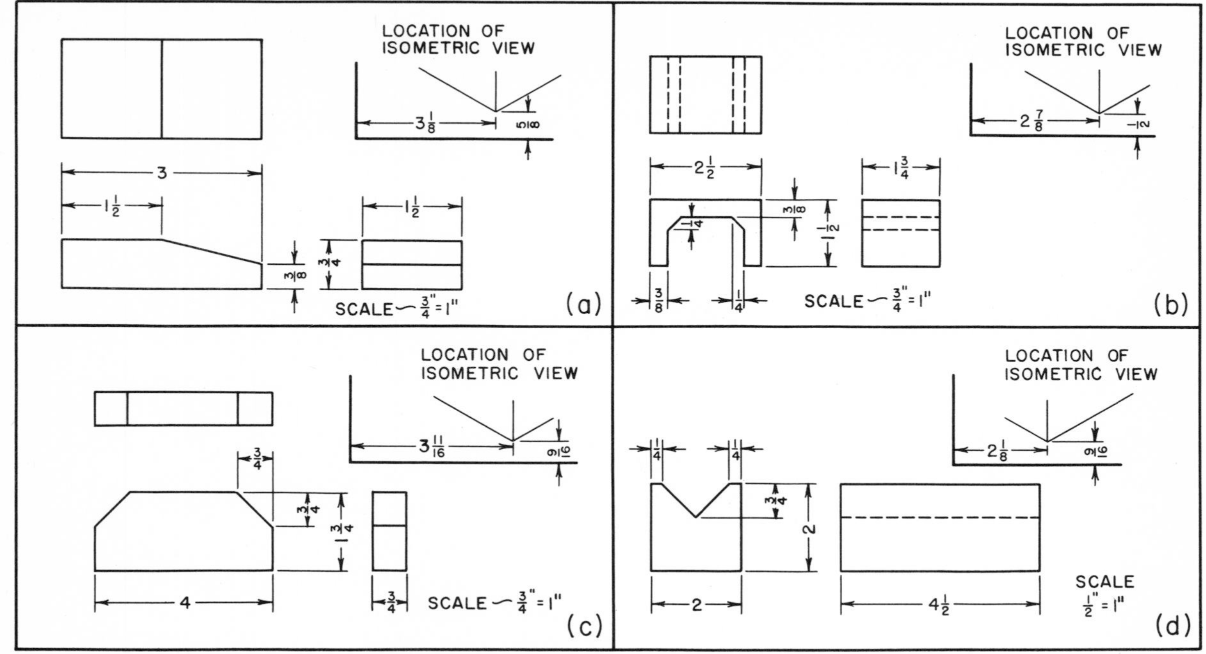

Fig. 7-6. Problems for isometric drawing.

isometric axes, and extension lines are projected in line with the surface or distance dimensioned, Fig. 7-5. Note that the dimension figures are also in line with the isometric axes.

DRAFTY SAYS: "Clean plate with art gum if needed before final finishing lines."

DRAFTING ACTIVITY

1. Divide your plate into four sections using the Plan A layout.
2. Use sections A and B and draw isometric views of two of the objects shown in Fig. 7-6, as assigned by your instructor.
3. Note the suggested location of the isometric axes for each. Use the full-size scale to locate the isometric axes, but use the scale indicated for drawing the isometric view.
4. Dimension the drawings.

ISOMETRIC CIRCLES AND ARCS

Because isometric surfaces are viewed at an angle, circles and arcs are not true. They are more elliptical in shape. Let's find out how they are drawn.

Procedure for drawing isometric circles and arcs: *

1. Locate and draw the center lines of the circle, Fig. 7-7a.
2. From the point of intersection of the center lines, measure the radii (plural form of radius), Fig. 7-7b.
3. From these radius points, draw construction lines which are perpendicular (90 deg.) to the other center line, Fig. 7-7c and d.
4. The intersections of these lines are the four centers for the isometric circle or ellipse, Fig. 7-7e.

***Courtesy A. Frank Nelson**

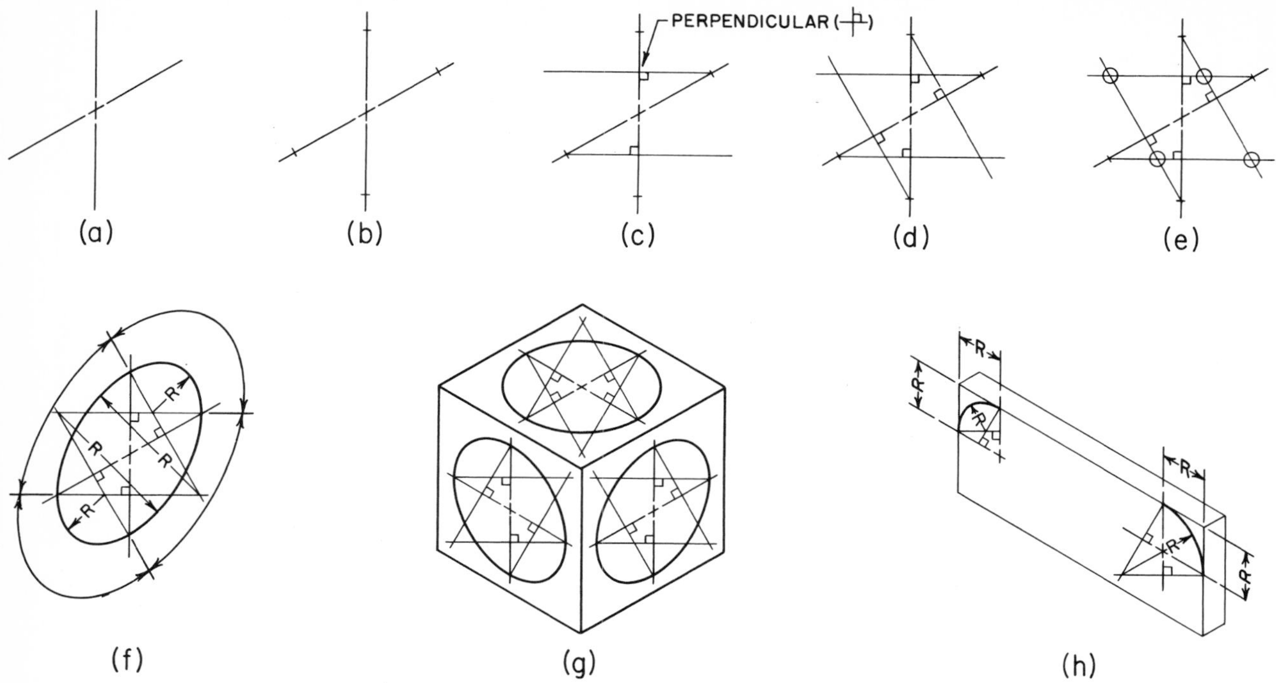

Fig. 7-7. Steps in drawing isometric circles and arcs.

5. Draw the isometric circle as shown in Fig. 7-7f. Circles in all three isometric planes are shown in Fig. 7-7g.
6. Draw arcs in the same manner as circles, using only the portion of the circle required, Fig. 7-7h.

DRAFTING ACTIVITY

1. In sections C and D, draw the isometric views of two of the problems shown in Fig. 7-8, as assigned by your instructor.
2. Dimension the drawings.

Fig. 7-8. Isometric circle and arc problems.

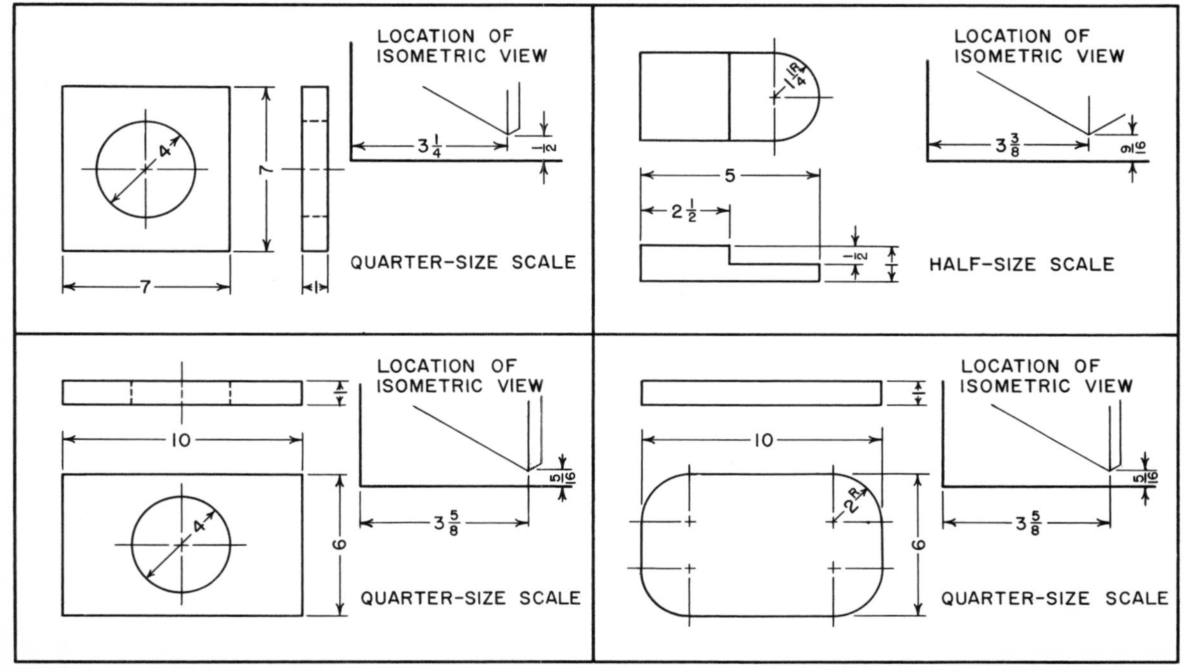

OBLIQUE DRAWINGS

Another type of pictorial drawing used in drafting is the oblique drawing. It has a front surface which is shown in its true size and shape, and a top and a side which usually slant back at an angle of 45 deg., but the angle can be 30 deg. or 60 deg., Fig. 7-9. This slanting of the top and side,

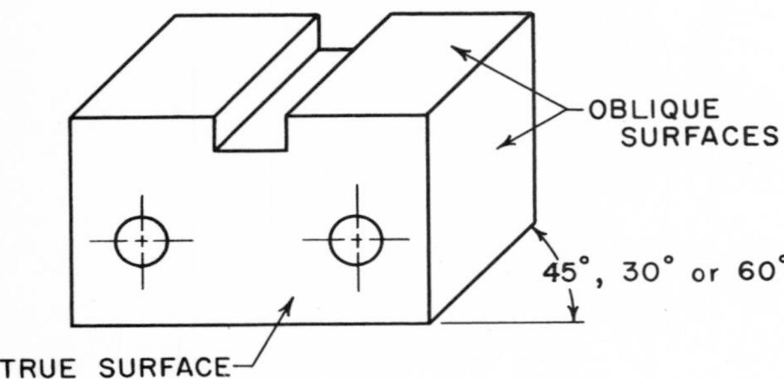

Fig. 7-9. Oblique drawing.

back from the front, is the meaning of the term oblique. This type of drawing is particularly useful when circles or arcs are to be shown and can be drawn in a front surface where they appear as true arcs or circles, rather than ellipses.

When the depth of the object, shown in the top and side surfaces, is true length, the drawing is called a cavalier oblique, Fig. 7-10a. This true length produces an object that appears unnatural, and the depth is sometimes foreshortened to one-half of its true length. This type of drawing is called cabinet oblique, Fig. 7-10b.

Procedure for constructing an oblique drawing:

1. Select the surface to be shown in the front face. Give consideration first to circles and arcs, next to long rectangular surfaces, Fig. 7-11.
2. Draw front view in its true size and shape, Fig. 7-12a.
3. Draw oblique lines (usually 45 deg.) to the right to form the top and right surfaces, Fig. 7-12b, or to the left for top and left surfaces, Fig. 7-12c.
4. Measure the depth on an oblique line,

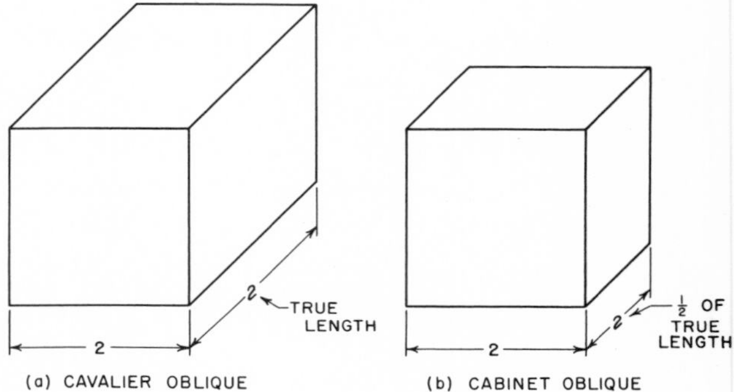

Fig. 7-10. Cavalier oblique and cabinet oblique drawings.

and "box" in the top and side surfaces, Fig. 7-12d.
5. Draw lines which are not parallel to the oblique axes by locating the end points (as in isometric drawing) and connecting these points by use of a straightedge, Fig. 7-12e.
6. Do not show hidden lines in oblique

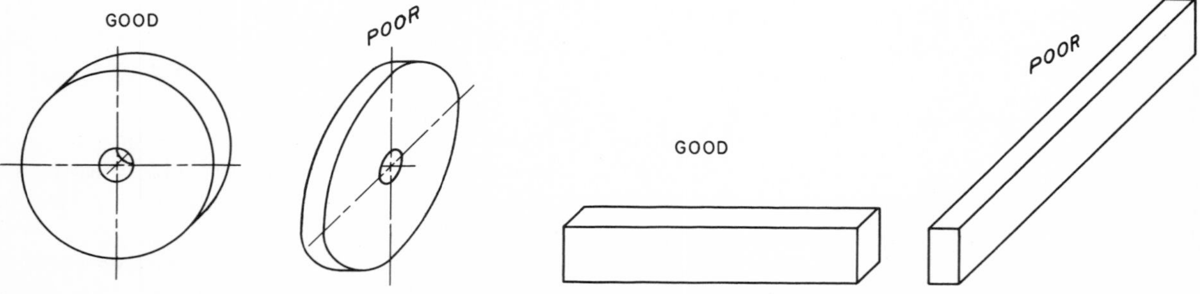

Fig. 7-11. Selection of the front surface in oblique drawings.

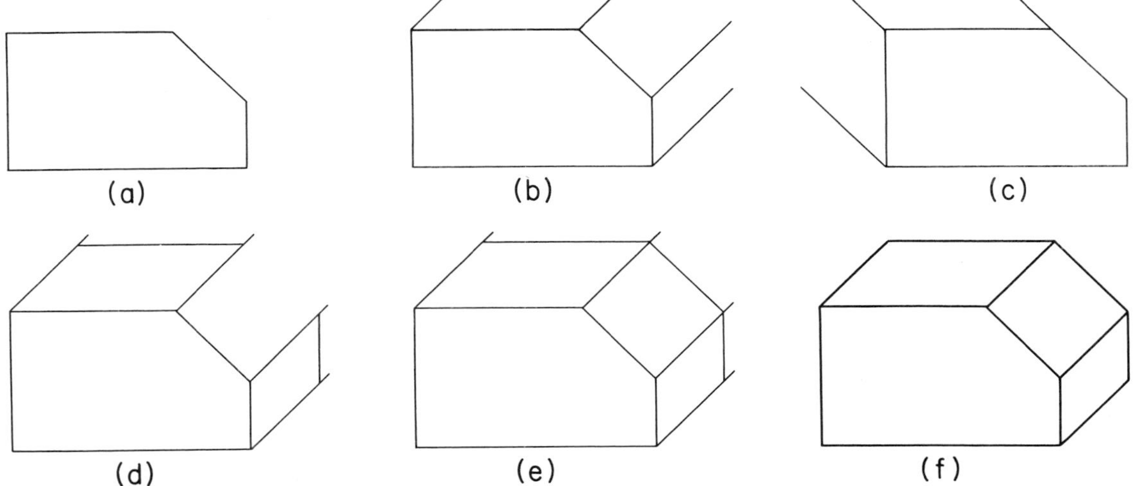

Fig. 7-12. Steps in constructing an oblique drawing.

drawings unless they are needed for clarity.

7. Darken all lines, Fig. 7-12f.

Oblique views may also be drawn as viewed from below the object. To do this, project the oblique lines downward from the front view, Fig. 7-13.

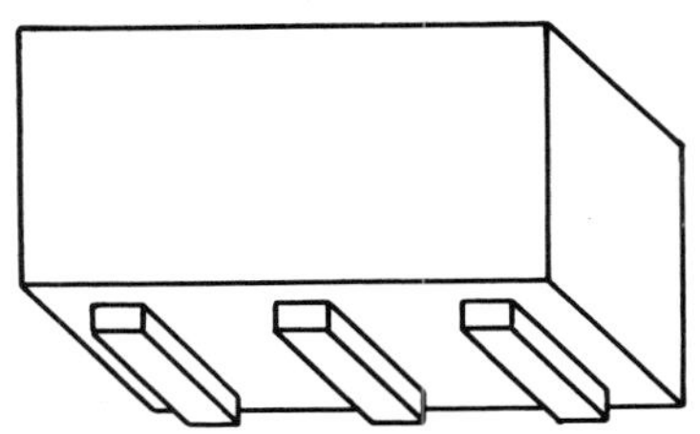

Fig. 7-13. Oblique drawing viewed from below the object.

DIMENSIONING OBLIQUE DRAWINGS

Dimension lines are parallel to the oblique axes and extension lines are projected in line with the surface or distance dimensioned, Fig. 7-14.

CIRCLES AND ARCS IN OBLIQUE

Since the front of an oblique drawing is a true view, as in a multiview drawing, all circles and arcs appear in their true shape.

To draw circles and arcs on oblique surfaces, follow the same procedure as given for drawing these in isometric views, Fig. 7-7. Only the angle of the center lines differs.

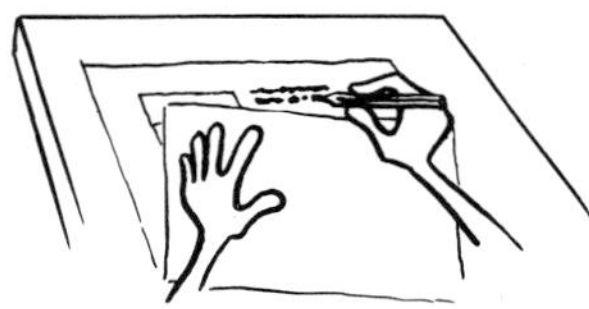

DRAFTY SAYS: "When lettering, protect drawing with extra sheet of paper."

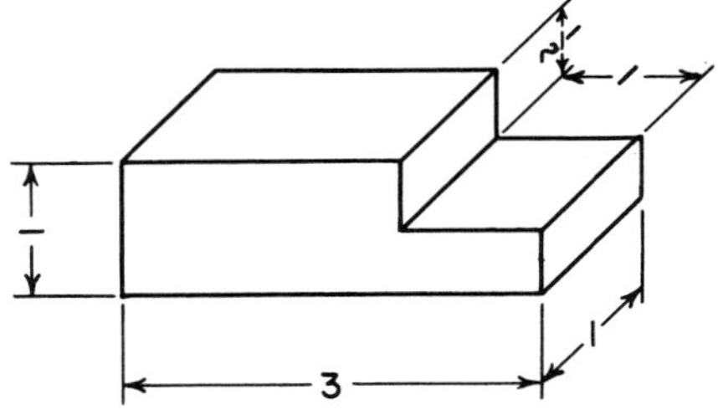

Fig. 7-14. Oblique dimensioning.

DRAFTING ACTIVITY

1. In sections A and B, draw oblique views of two of the problems shown in Fig. 7-15, as assigned by your instructor.
2. Estimate the location of the axes so as to approximately center each drawing. A freehand sketch will

aid you in centering your drawing.

3. Dimension the drawings.

PERSPECTIVE DRAWINGS

The perspective is a third type of pictorial drawing and is more natural in appearance than either the isometric or oblique drawings. The construction of this type of drawing, if done properly, is complicated and lengthy. You will get experience with this type if you take an advanced drafting course.

For illustrating the different types of pictorial drawings, the jewel box is shown in four pictorial views, Fig. 7-16.

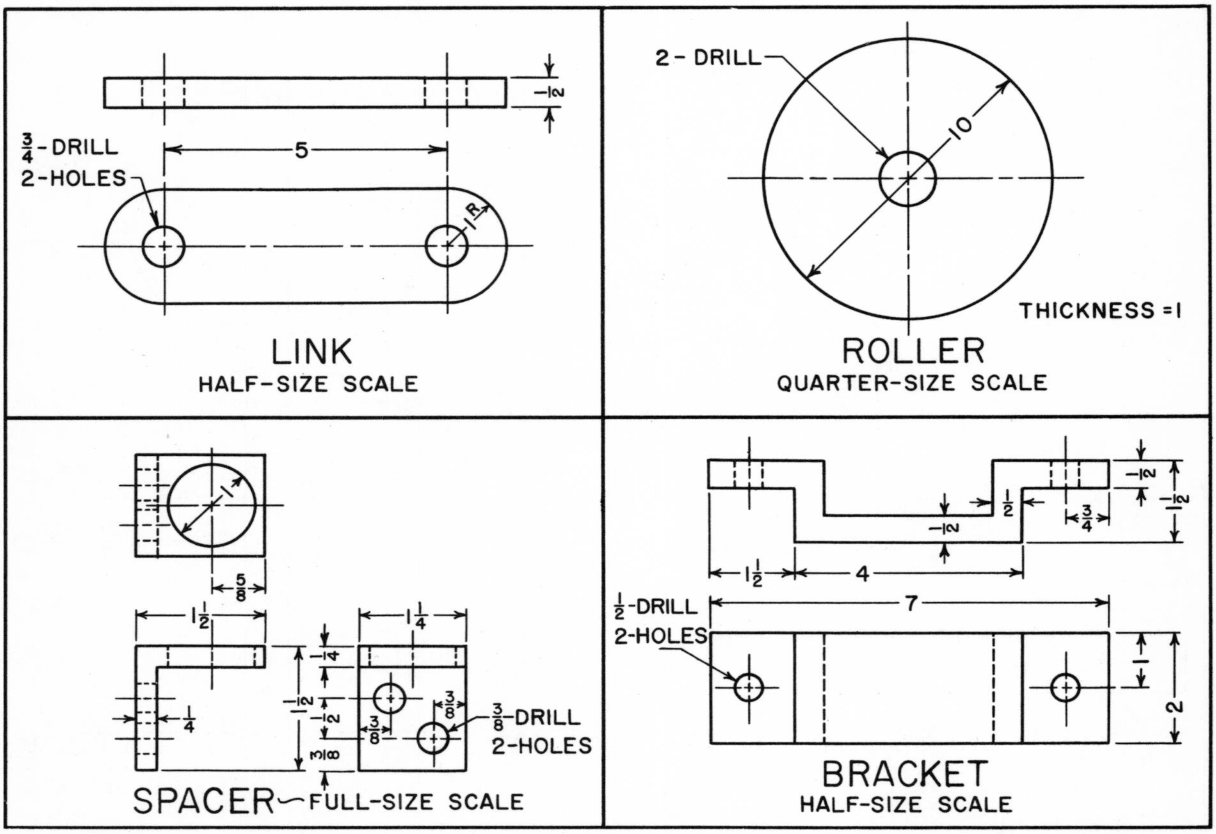

Fig. 7-15. Problems for oblique drawing.

DRAFTING ACTIVITY

1. In sections C and D, draw addition-

Fig. 7-16. Jewel box in four pictorial views.

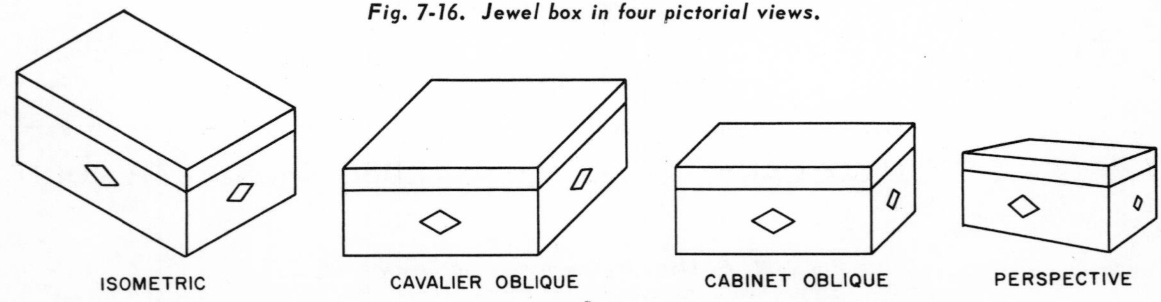

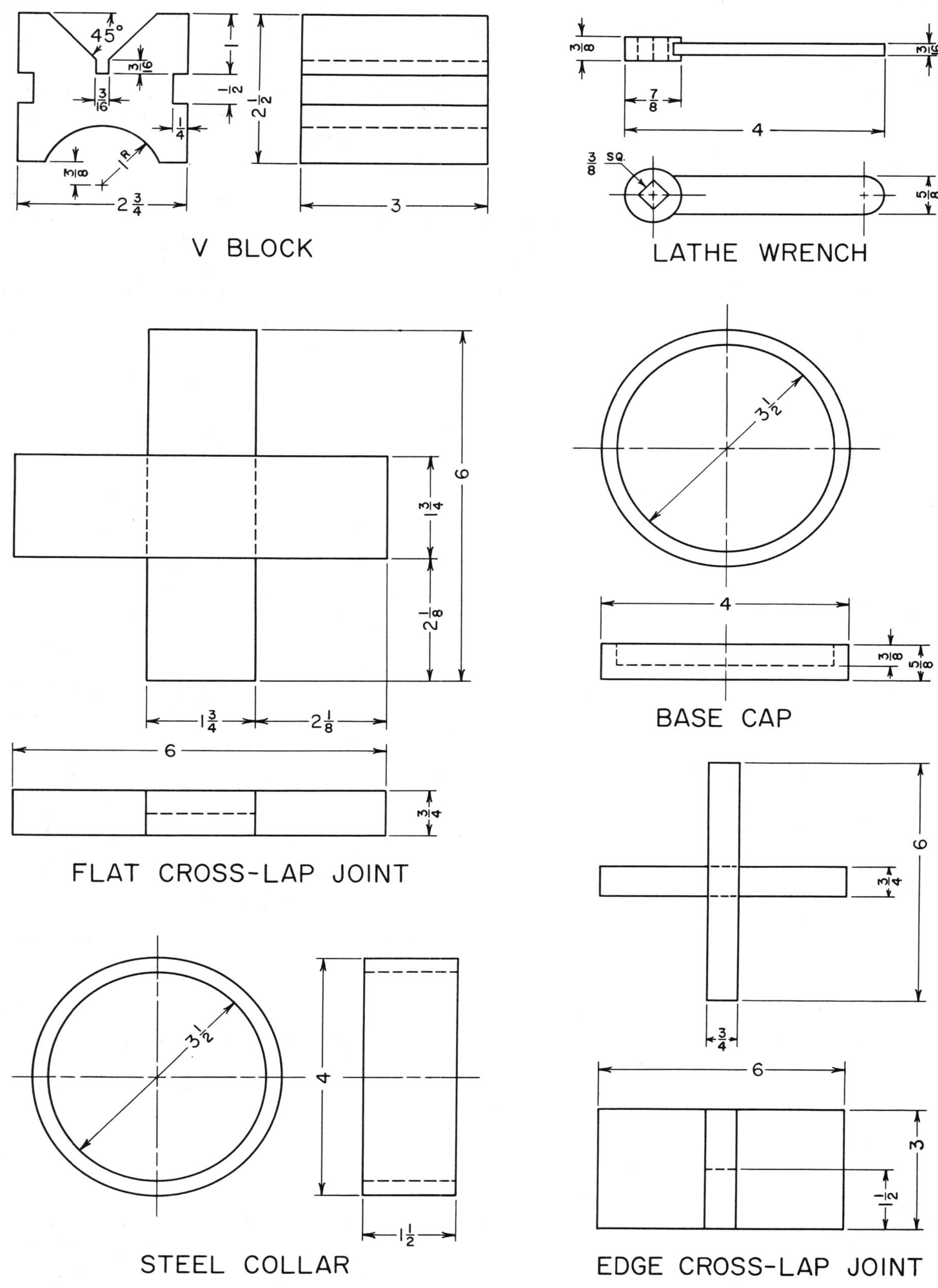

Fig. 7-17. Problems for isometric or oblique drawing.
(Additional problems on pages 109, 110.)

al isometric or oblique drawings as assigned by your instructor from the problems shown in Fig. 7-17.

2. Estimate the location of the axes so as to approximately center each drawing.

QUIZ - UNIT 7

1. What are the common types of pictorial drawings?
2. For what purposes are pictorial drawings used?
3. What angle is used for horizontal lines in isometric drawings? In oblique?
4. How does the cabinet oblique differ from the cavalier oblique drawing?
5. How are isometric and oblique drawings dimensioned?

NEW WORDS FOR YOU TO USE

1. Isometric (i-so-met'rik)
2. Oblique (ob-lek')
3. Perspective (per-spek'tiv)
4. Ellipse (e-lips')

All manufactured products, such as this turbine assembly, were first created on the drawing board. (Westinghouse)

ELECTRICAL DRAFTING

1. What types of drawings are used in the field of electricity?
2. How are electrical diagrams drawn?
3. What symbols are used in electrical diagrams?

Electrical devices and circuits would be difficult to draw as pictorial or multi-view drawings, Fig. 8-1. Instead, electrical diagrams are used more often in constructing radios, hi-fi equipment, electric motors, and other electrical projects. The use of these diagrams speeds up electrical drafting and makes the reading of these drawings much easier.

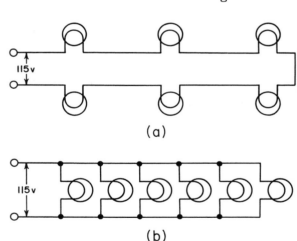

Fig. 8-1. A one-tube radio.

The purpose of this unit in electrical drafting is to acquaint you with the types of electrical circuits and the techniques of drawing electrical diagrams. The skill and knowledge needed in electrical drafting is not so much in the area of drafting as it is in the understanding of electricity. Your study of electrical drafting will help you in your understanding of electricity, and a study of electricity will bring more meaning to your work in electrical drafting.

TYPES OF CIRCUITS

A circuit is a path along which the electric current flows from the negative side of the power source through the circuit and on to the positive side of the power source, completing the circuit. There are several types of electrical circuits which may be used when two or more devices or

115v

(a)

115v

(b)

Fig. 8-2. Lights in series (a) and in parallel (b).

NOTE: The illustrations of the one-tube radio, the superheterodyne receiver, and the power supply used in this unit are of projects in Electronics, by Howard Gerrish, which is one of the texts in this Industrial Arts Series.

controls are to be placed in the circuit. Common circuits are the series circuit, parallel circuit, and combinations of these two circuits.

The series circuit provides a single, continuous path in which the current flows. The electrical devices in a series circuit are connected one after another and the current flows through the first device, through the second, and so on until it returns to the power source. A string of lights wired in series is shown in Fig. 8-2a. Some Christmas tree lights are wired in series. In this type of circuit, when one light burns out, the remaining lights will not burn, because the circuit is broken.

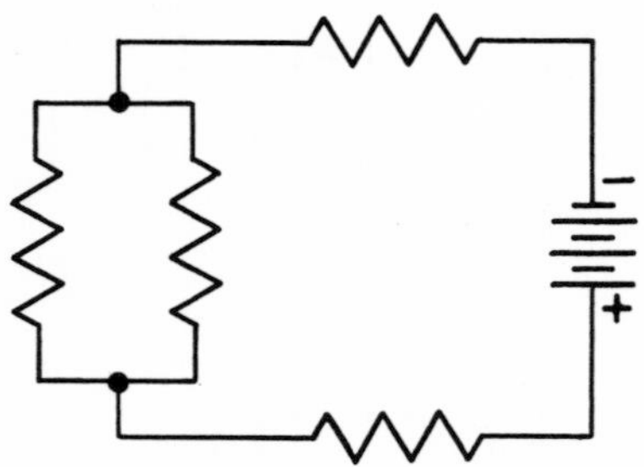

Fig. 8-3. A combination circuit of resistors in series and parallel.

In the parallel circuit, the current has two or more paths to follow. Each device in a parallel circuit has access to the power source and, therefore, will continue to operate regardless of failure in another device. A string of lights wired in parallel is shown in Fig. 8-2b. More expensive Christmas tree lights are wired in this manner. Parallel circuits are used in house wiring.

A combination circuit of resistors in series and parallel is illustrated in Fig. 8-3.

Fig. 8-4. Wiring diagram of the one-tube radio shown in Fig. 8-1.

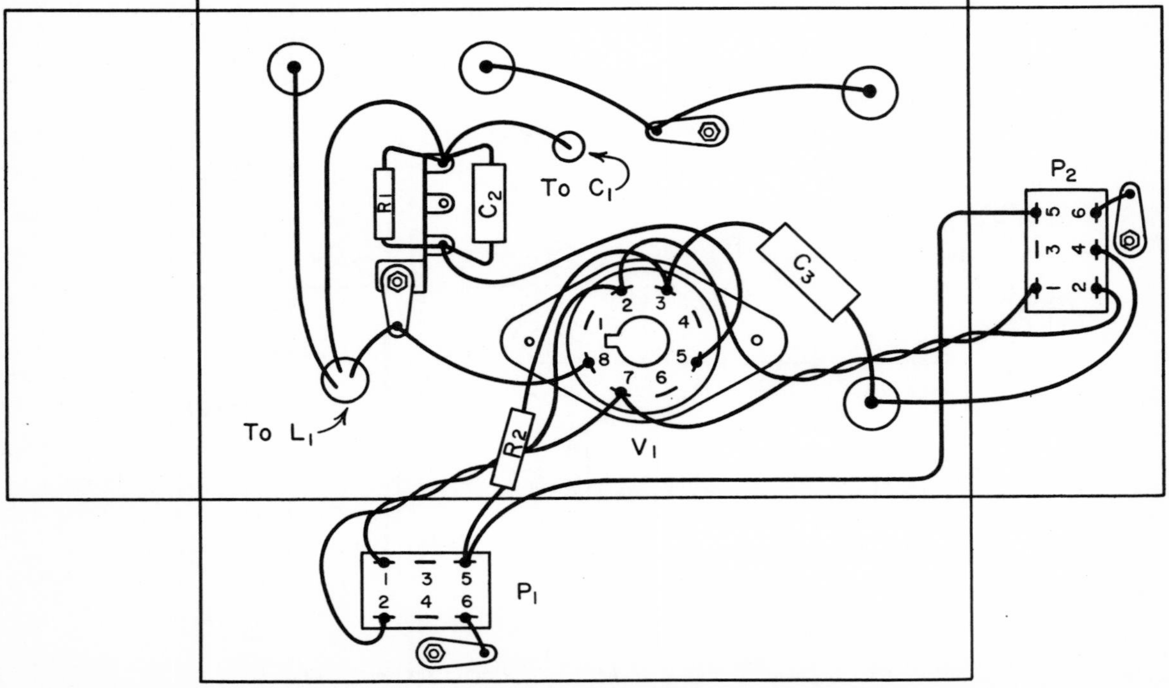

These circuits are discussed in more detail in the text, Electronics, by Gerrish.

TYPES OF ELECTRICAL DIAGRAMS

Wiring diagrams are pictorial drawings of electrical assemblies showing how the various parts are arranged and connected together, Fig. 8-4. This type of diagram is used by hobbyists and electrical repairmen to install and service electrical devices. Electrical diagrams for houses are a form of wiring diagrams, Fig. 8-5.

Schematic diagrams are similar to wiring diagrams, except electrical symbols

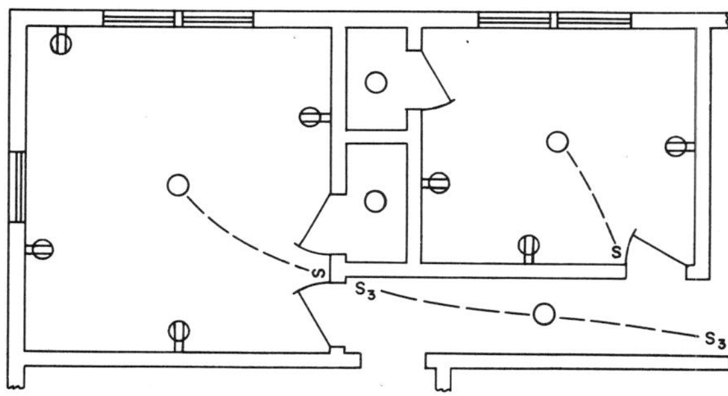

Fig. 8-5. House wiring diagram.

instead of pictures are used for representing parts, Fig. 8-6. Schematic diagrams are used to show the functional relationship of electrical parts to each other and to the entire circuit. They do not show the location of parts or wiring connections as do wiring diagrams.

Block diagrams are another type of electrical drawing. They show the relationship of the various sections of an electrical device, such as the one-tube radio receiver in Fig. 8-7. Such a drawing may

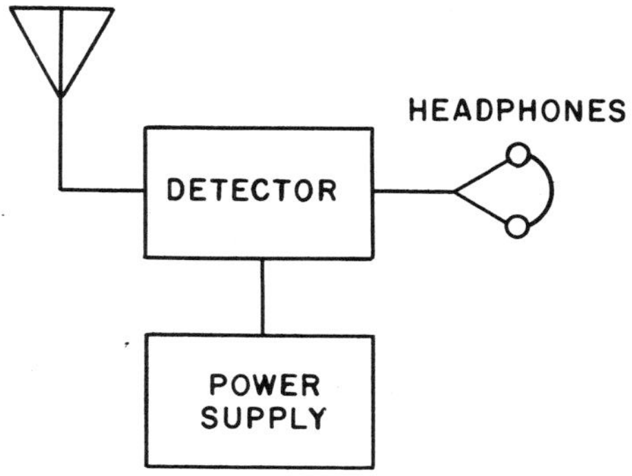

Fig. 8-7. Block diagram of the one-tube radio shown in Fig. 8-1.

be used as a simplified drawing of complex electrical parts to show the function of the various sections, and for trouble shooting. The more complex the circuit, the more useful the block diagram. A block diagram of a superheterodyne receiver is shown in Fig. 8-8.

You will appreciate the uses of each of these electrical drawings as your knowl-

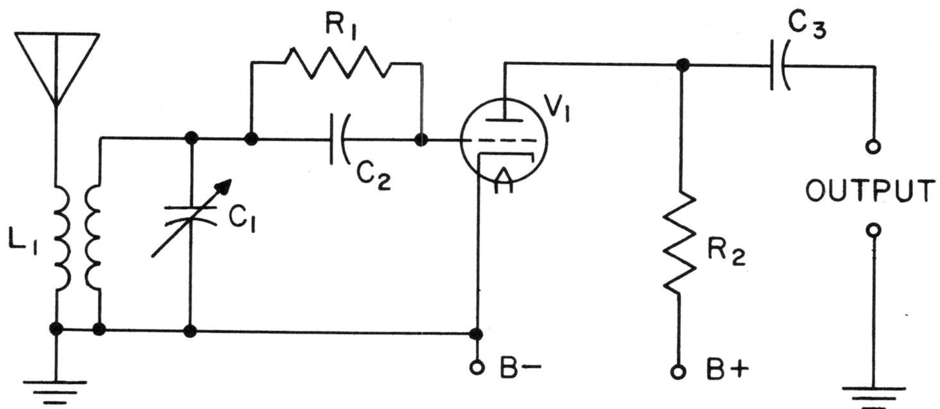

Fig. 8-6. Schematic diagram of the one-tube radio shown in Fig. 8-1.

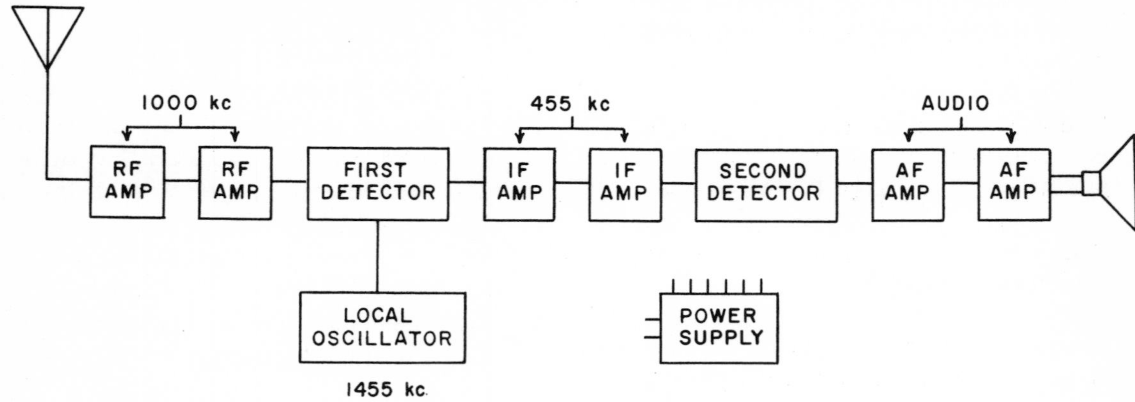

Fig. 8-8. Block diagram of a superheterodyne receiver.

edge of electricity and electronics increases.

HOUSE WIRING

The electrical diagrams on house plans are usually included on a scale drawing of the floor plan, as in Fig. 8-5. See Fig. 11-9, page 87, for electrical symbols used in house wiring. In planning the wiring for a house, attention should be given to the following: (1) location of switches near doorways, halls, stairways, and other convenient places; (2) location of ceiling outlets where desired in rooms, closets, halls, and stairwells; (3) location of convenience outlets on walls for table lamps, radios, television, clocks, kitchen appliances, shop equipment, etc. Lines are drawn from switches to the outlets they control, but other circuits are planned by the electrical contractor. The number of switches, outlets, etc., can be counted directly, and the amount of wire needed can be estimated from the location of the various devices on the scale drawing.

DRAWING ELECTRICAL DIAGRAMS

Unlike other types of drawing you have been doing, electrical diagrams are not drawn to any particular size. The diagram should be large enough to show clearly the various parts, and no larger. The symbols themselves may vary in size, but they should be drawn correctly and in proportion, Fig. 8-9. All lines are drawn about the weight of visible object lines, except when some part is to be emphasized, and then a heavier line is used.

DRAFTING ACTIVITY

No. 1

1. Use the Plan A plate layout and draw as many of the electrical

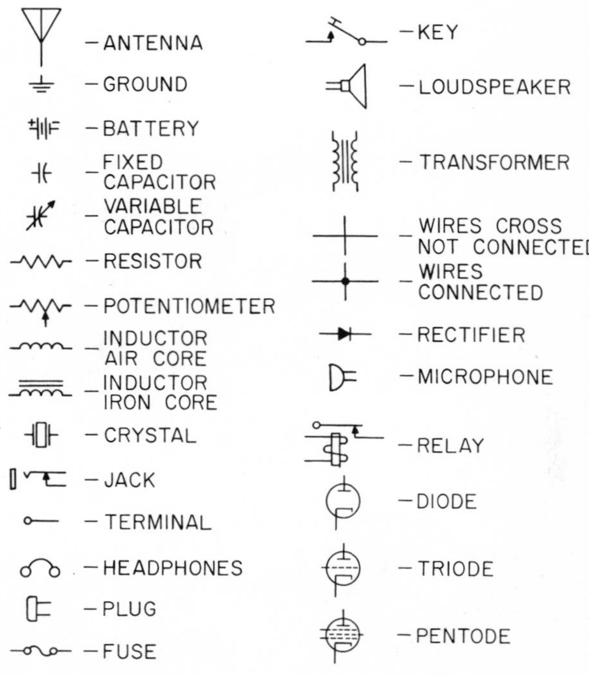

Fig. 8-9. Electrical symbols.

symbols, Fig. 11-9, and the electrical symbols, Fig. 8-9, as space will permit.

No. 2

1. Draw a wiring diagram for a light controlled by two 3-way switches. See Fig. 11-9, page 87 for proper symbols.
2. Place on a full-sized sheet, using the Plan A plate layout.

No. 3

1. If you have had instruction in electronics, try your skill at drawing a wiring diagram of the power supply illustrated by the schematic diagram, Fig. 8-10.

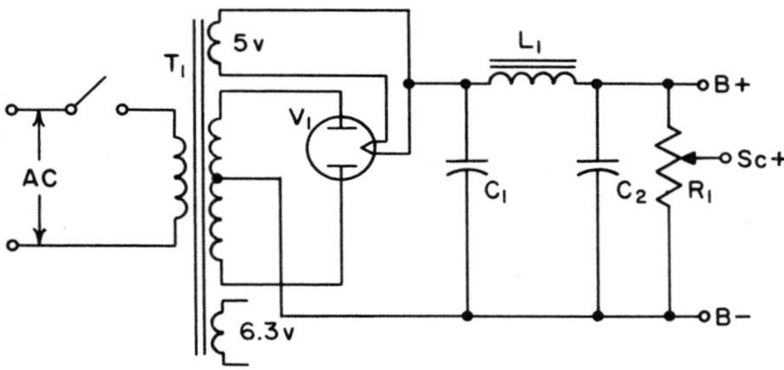

Fig. 8-10. Schematic diagram of a power supply.

QUIZ - UNIT 8

1. How do the series circuit and the parallel circuit differ?
2. What are the three types of electrical diagrams and how do they differ?
3. What is the purpose of each type of electrical diagram?
4. What type of electrical diagram is most useful in trouble shooting?
5. Electrical diagrams on house plans are known as what type of electrical diagrams?
6. What should electrical diagrams for house wiring include?
7. How large should electrical symbols be drawn? What line weight should be used?

NEW WORDS FOR YOU TO USE

1. Series (ser'ez)
2. Circuit (sur'kit)
3. Diagram (di'a-gram)
4. Schematic (ske-mat'ik)
5. Superheterodyne (su- per - het'er-o-din)

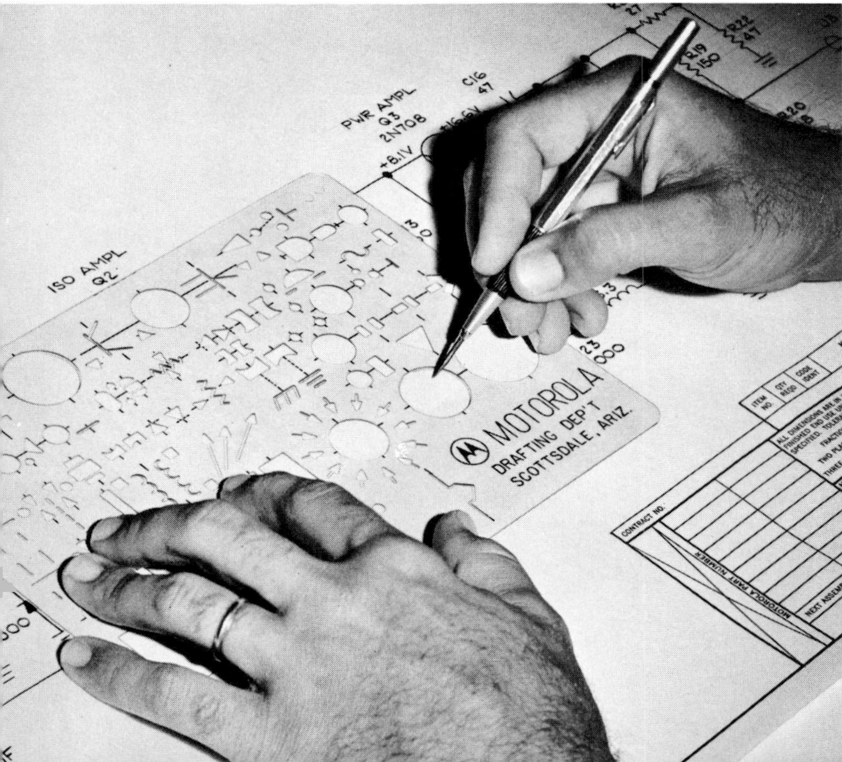

Draftsman using an electronic symbol template. (Motorola)

Fig. 9-1. Geometry applied to bridge construction. (California Div. of Highways)

GEOMETRICAL CONSTRUCTION

1. How does geometry relate to drafting?
2. What is a polygon?
3. How are pentagons, hexagons, and octagons constructed?
4. How is a 5-point star constructed?

In our daily activities we come in contact with many applications of geometry. One example is shown in Fig. 9-1. You have already learned to construct a good many geometrical figures: arcs, circles, squares, and triangles. In addition you have learned how to divide a space, or a line, into an equal number of parts. You will also want to learn how to draw polygons. Polygons are figures having many sides, especially figures with more than four sides. The Pentagon in Washington, D. C. is an example of the use of a polygon in architecture, Fig. 9-2.

Fig. 9-2. The Pentagon in Washington, D. C. (Official U. S. Air Force Photo)

CONSTRUCTING A PENTAGON AND A 5-POINT STAR

The pentagon (5 sides) and the 5-point star are constructed as follows:

1. Draw a circle equal to the size of pentagon desired, Fig. 9-3.

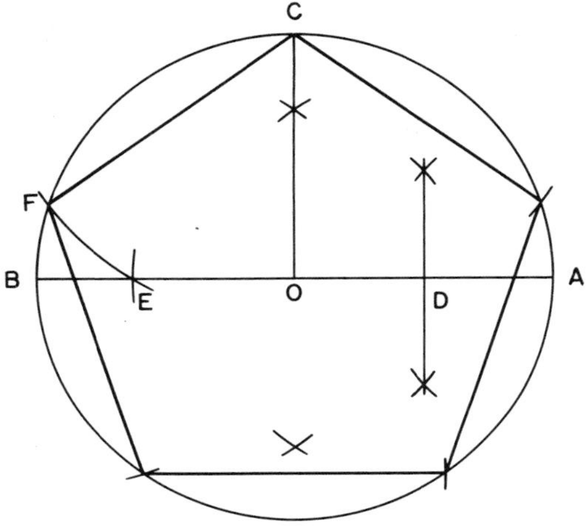

Fig. 9-3. Construction of a pentagon.

2. Construct diameter, AB and radius OC perpendicular to AB.
3. Bisect line AO to find center point D.
4. Draw CE using point D as the center.

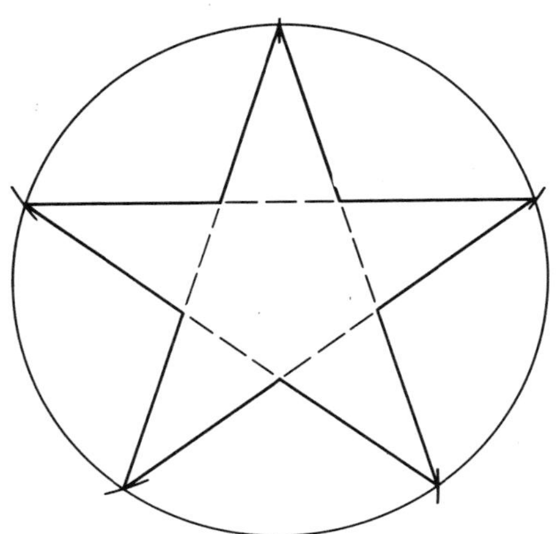

Fig. 9-4. Five-point star.

6. Draw arc EF from center point C.
7. Draw the line CF.
8. Lay off the four remaining sides, equal to CF, around the circle.
9. Connect the points around the circumference to form a pentagon.

To form a 5-point star locate the five points as above and connect the points as shown in Fig. 9-4.

DRAFTING ACTIVITY

1. Lay out plate using Plan A border and divide into four sections.
2. In section A, construct a pentagon inside a 3" circle. Make light construction lines and darken pentagon when completed.
3. In section B, construct a 5-point star inside a 3" circle.

CONSTRUCTING HEXAGONS AND OCTAGONS

The hexagon (6 sides) and the octagon (8 sides) can be constructed by first drawing a circle equal to the polygon desired. The sides are located as shown in Fig. 9-5.

If the hexagon and octagon are to be drawn on material where the T-square and triangles cannot be used, follow the procedures in Fig. 9-6.

DRAFTING ACTIVITY

1. In section C, construct a hexagon within a 3" circle, using only the compass and a straightedge.
2. In section D, construct an octagon inside a 3" square. You may use the T-square and the triangle to construct the square, but use only the compass and a straightedge to construct the octagon.

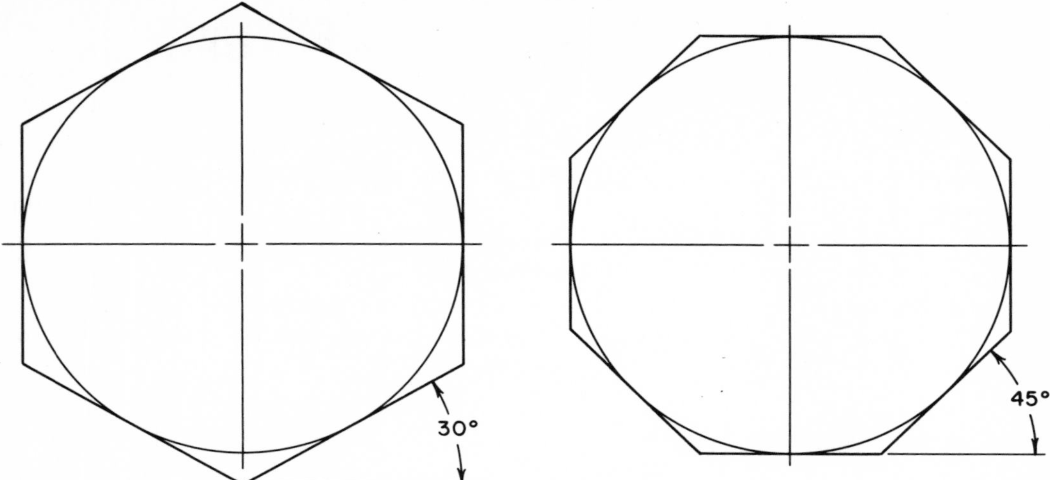

Fig. 9-5. Constructing the hexagon and octagon with the T-square and triangles.

QUIZ - UNIT 9

1. Name as many geometrical figures as you can and give an example of the use of each in life.
2. What are polygons?
3. Of what importance is accuracy in laying out geometrical forms?
4. What use can you make of geometrical construction?

NEW WORDS FOR YOU TO USE

1. Geometry (je-om'e-tri)
2. Polygon (pol'i-gon)

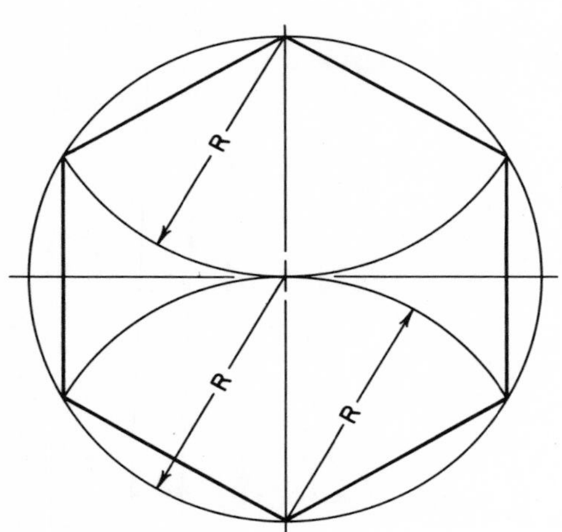

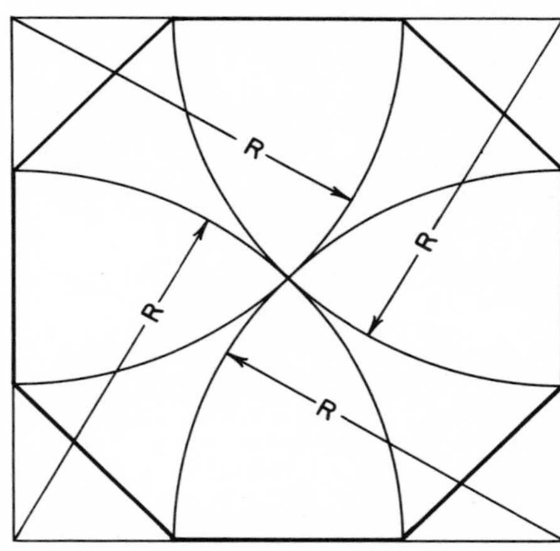

Fig. 9-6. Constructing the hexagon and octagon with the compass.

SHEET METAL DRAFTING

1. What is a "stretchout?"

2. How are sheet metal patterns developed?

3. How will you use sheet metal drafting?

One type of sheet metal drafting is used by the men who lay out air conditioning and heating ducts for buildings, Fig. 10-1. The modern water tower shown in Fig. 10-2, is also a product of sheet metal draftsmen's skill.

The purpose of sheet metal drafting is to develop full-size patterns or "stretch-

Fig. 10-1. Sheet Metal ducts. (Lennox Industries, Inc.)

outs" for sheet metal objects. In your shop work, you will be constructing projects of sheet metal, and a knowledge of how these patterns are developed will be useful.

Let's see how some sheet metal patterns are developed.

RECTANGULAR LAYOUTS

One of the simplest sheet metal patterns to develop is the rectangular box. A layout for a rectangular box such as a pan or a radio chassis is developed as follows:

1. Draw the bottom of the pan (or top of radio chassis), Fig. 10-3a.

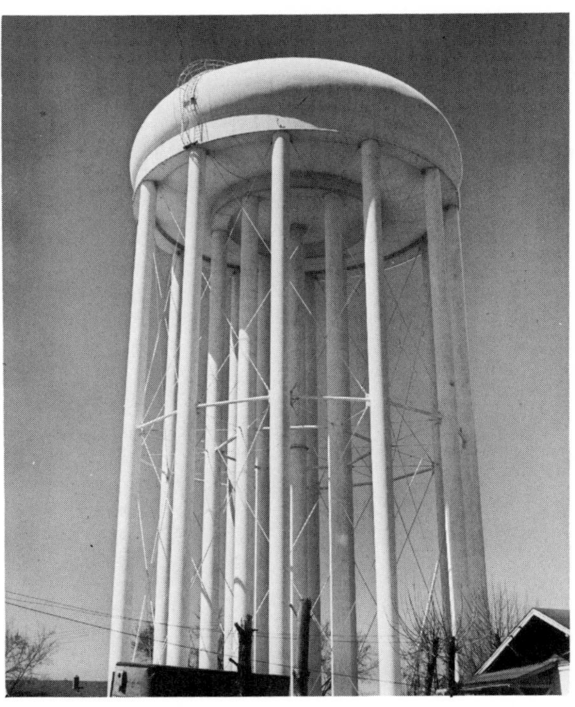

Fig. 10-2. Sheet metal patterns were required for this water tower. (Massie--Missouri Resources Division)

2. Add to each edge the height of the sides, Fig. 10-3b.
3. Add material for hems and seams if needed, Fig. 10-3c.
4. Cut out the pattern, then fold, and assemble with cellophane tape as a

paper model; or transfer to metal, cut out, fold and assemble, Fig. 10-3d.

DRAFTING ACTIVITY

1. Develop the pattern for the radio chassis as shown in Fig. 10-4.

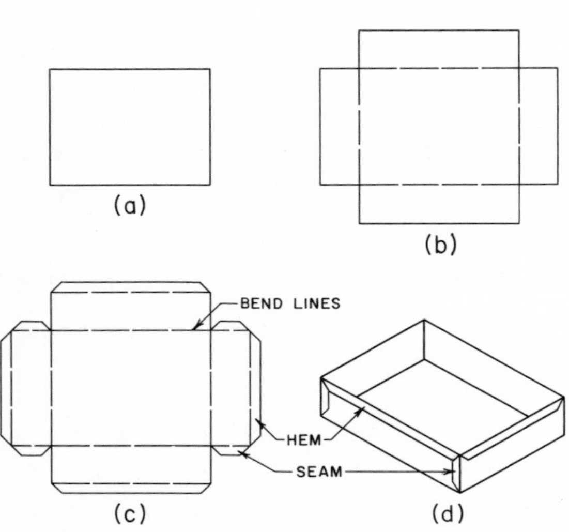

Fig. 10-3. Steps in laying out a rectangular pattern.

2. Letter your name on the top of the chassis pattern.
3. Cut out and fold to shape.
4. Material could be added to close

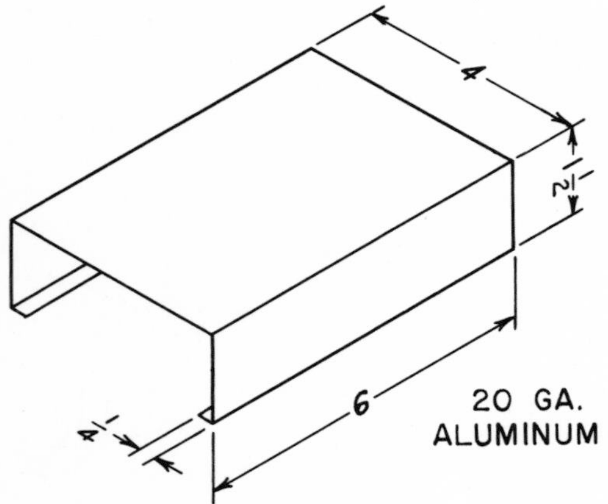

Fig. 10-4. Radio chassis.

the ends, if desired.
5. This is the pattern for the chassis used in the projects in the <u>Electronics</u> text, by Gerrish.

LAYOUT FOR A PRISM

A prism is a solid object with parallel sides and bases which are identical, such as the hexagonal prism (a) and the octagonal prism (b) shown in Fig. 10-5.

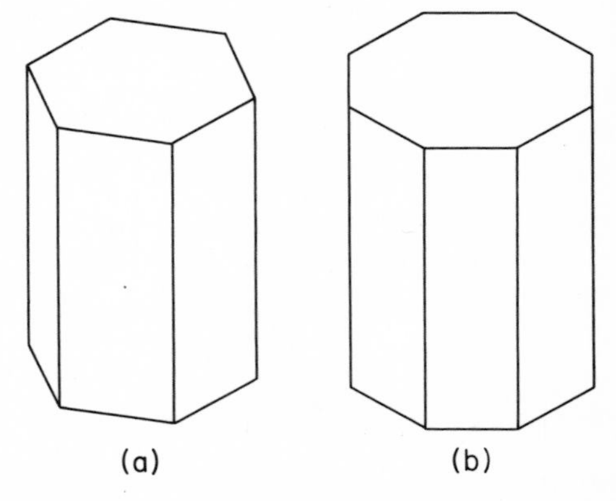

Fig. 10-5. Hexagonal and octagonal prisms.

The layout for a prism is as follows:

1. Draw the hexagon (or octagon) near one edge of your layout sheet, Fig. 10-6a. (See page 74 for the construction of polygons).

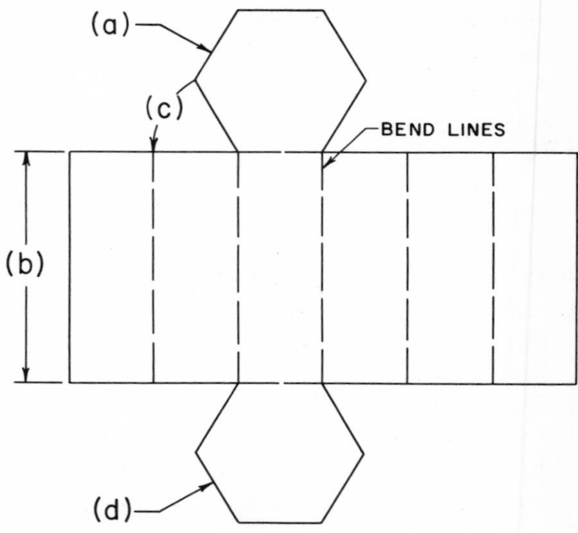

Fig. 10-6. Layout for a prism.

2. Draw lines representing the height of the prism, Fig. 10-6b.
3. Lay off the distances for the sides with dividers, Fig. 10-6c.
4. Draw the other base, Fig. 10-6d.
5. Add to layout for seams if necessary.
6. Cut out pattern, then fold, and assemble with cellophane tape; or transfer to sheet metal; cut out, fold, and assemble.

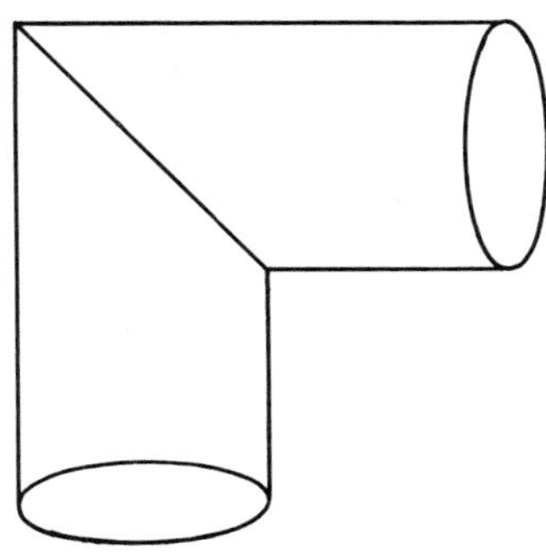

Fig. 10-7. Sheet metal elbow.

DRAFTING ACTIVITY

1. Develop the pattern for the hexagonal or the octagonal prisms, shown in Fig. 10-5.
2. Dimensions of the prisms are: 1-1/2 in. across the flat sides of the hexagon and octagon; 2-1/2 in. in height.
3. Letter your name on one side of the prism.

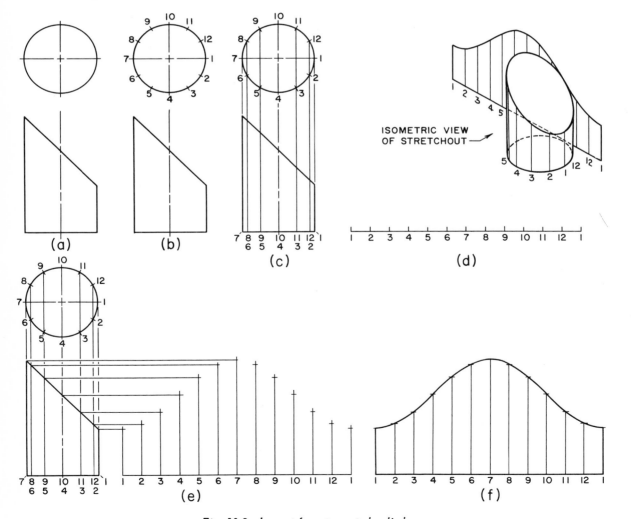

Fig. 10-8. Layout for a truncated cylinder.

4. Cut out and assemble with cellophane tape.

LAYOUT FOR A TRUNCATED CYLINDER

Have you noticed all of the twists and turns in the pipes of a hot-air furnace? Such pipes, which are cut off at an angle, or truncated, are called elbows when joined, Fig. 10-7. Do you wonder how it is possible to cut the pipe at just the proper angle to make it fit? The secret of this layout is not difficult if you follow this procedure:

1. Observe first, the isometric view of the layout (called stretchout) in the upper right-hand corner of Fig. 10-8.
2. Draw the top and front view as shown in Fig. 10-8a.
3. Divide the circular (top) view into a number of equal parts, say 12, Fig. 10-8b.
4. Project these points to the front view, Fig. 10-8c.
5. Draw the stretchout line 1-1 and step off on line 1-1, the 12 distances in the top view with dividers, Fig. 10-8d. This should equal the circumference of the cylinder.
6. Project perpendiculars up from these points, Fig. 10-8e.
7. Project the height of each line in the front view to the stretchout. Note that two lines are represented in the stretchout by one line in the front view, Fig. 10-8e.
8. Sketch a light curve first, and then, using the French curve, join these points with a smooth curve, Fig. 10-8f.
9. Add material for seams if needed.

If you have studied Unit 5, you have already had some experience with auxiliary views. The auxiliary surface of the truncated cylinder is developed as follows:

1. Construct the auxiliary center line 1-7 parallel to the inclined surface, Fig. 10-9.
2. Project the points which divide the circle into equal parts from the inclined surface to the auxiliary view.
3. Transfer the widths from the top view to the auxiliary, using the dividers.
4. Sketch a light curve through these points. Finish with the French curve.

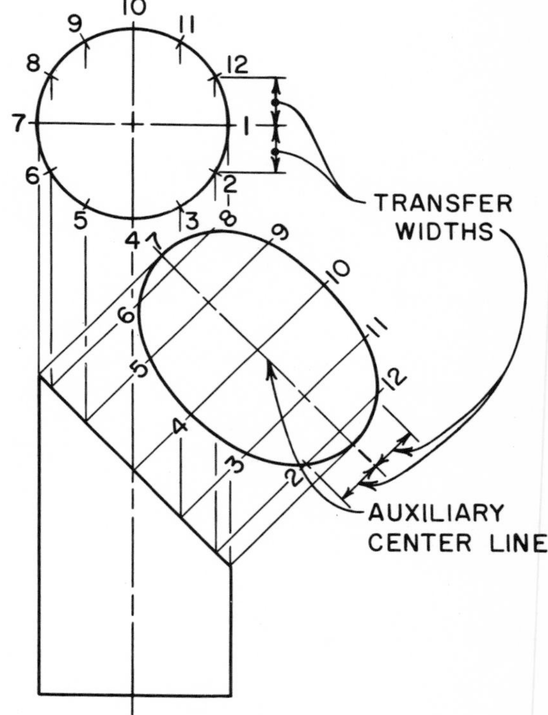

Fig. 10-9. Development of auxiliary surface.

5. Cut out and assemble pieces; or transfer to metal, cut out and assemble.

By omitting the auxiliary cap and laying out two pipe sections, with a 45 deg. cut, (the second section could be traced from the first) a right-elbow pipe joint could be formed, Fig. 10-7. This method of cylindrical development can be used

also in laying out a sugar scoop, Fig. 10-10.

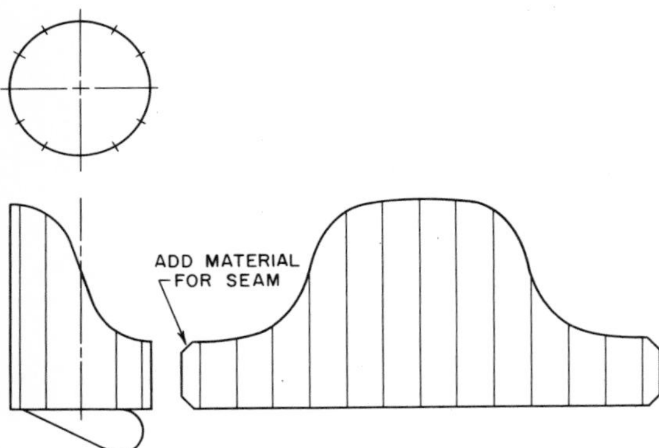

Fig. 10-10. Sugar scoop.

DRAFTING ACTIVITY

1. Develop a pattern for the truncated cylinder in Fig. 10-11.
2. Letter your name on the cylinder.
3. Trace a second section from the first, cut out and assemble as a right-elbow pipe; or develop the auxiliary cap and assemble as a truncated cylinder, as assigned by your instructor.

LAYOUT FOR A CONE

In your metal work in the shop, you probably will be making a funnel or some

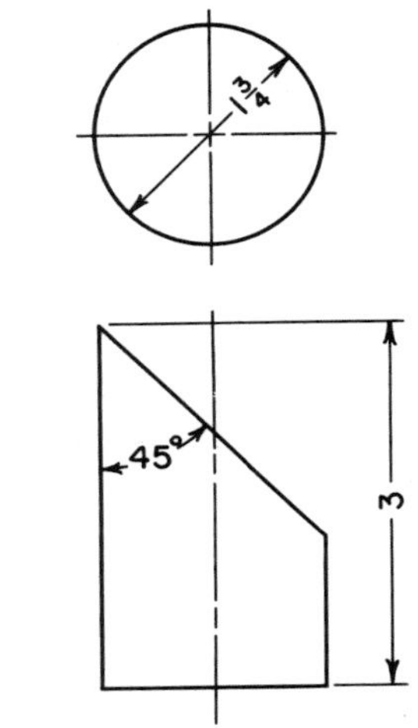

Fig. 10-11. Truncated cylinder.

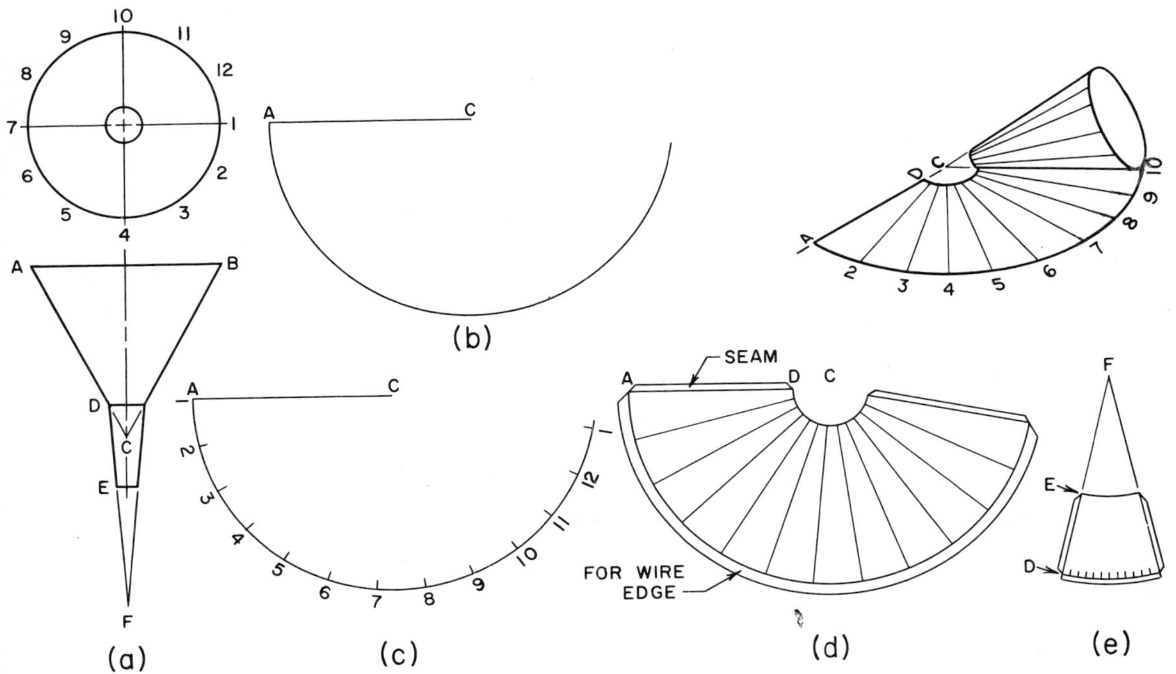

Fig. 10-12. Layout for a cone.

other cone-shaped object of sheet metal. You can lay out any of these cone-shaped objects by following this procedure:

1. Draw two views of the object showing its size and shape, Fig. 10-12a.
2. Draw the stretchout with AC as the radius, Fig. 10-12b.
3. Transfer the equal spaces representing the circumference in the top view to the stretchout, Fig. 10-12c.
4. Use the distance CD to draw the arc which forms the lower edge of the funnel body, Fig. 10-12d.

DRAFTY SAYS: "Always keep your pencil sharp. You can't do good work with a dull pencil."

5. Add material for the seam on sides and for the wire edge.
6. Make stretchout for spout in similar manner, Fig. 10-12e.

DRAFTING ACTIVITY

1. Develop the pattern for the funnel or megaphone shown in Fig. 10-13.
2. Letter your name on the pattern.

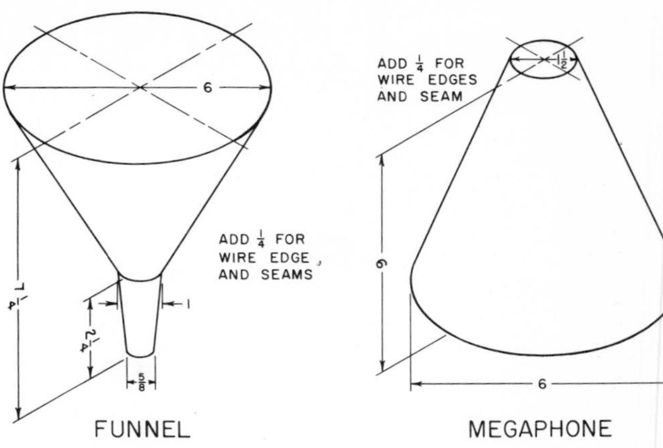

Fig. 10-13. Funnel and megaphone problems.

3. Cut out the pattern and assemble with cellophane tape. (Since this pattern may be used later in your metal work, allow for wire edges and seams).

QUIZ, - UNIT 10

1. Why are sheet metal drawings frequently referred to as "stretchouts?"
2. Name several types of workmen who use sheet metal patterns.
3. Why are patterns laid out full-size?
4. In making a stretchout for a cylindrical object, how is the length of the stretchout measured? Is there another way in which this could be obtained?

NEW WORDS FOR YOU TO USE

1. Cylinder (sil'in-der)
2. Prism (priz'm)
3. Truncated (trung'kat-ed)

Fig. 11-1. Traditional and contemporary styles of house architecture. Upper left--Dutch Colonial; upper right--Cape Cod; lower left--Modern; lower right--multi-level. (Better Homes and Gardens Magazine)

ARCHITECTURAL DRAFTING

1. What is architechtural drafting?
2. How do architectural styles differ?
3. What types of drawings are used in architectural work?

The special field of drafting which deals with the preparation of drawings for commercial and public buildings as well as for houses, is known as architectural drafting. The planning of any structure requires three things: (1) design of the exterior and interior of the building; (2) preparation of drawings showing details of construction; and (3) written specifications (sometimes called "specs") which provide a description of such things as quality of materials to be used, kinds of finish to be applied to floors and walls, etc., kinds of hardware, and types of electrical fixtures.

In many states, the above work is done by licensed architects. However, there is much the home owner can do in the preliminary planning of a new house or in the planning of alterations for his present house.

You may find that you will have a real interest in architectural drafting, so let's get started!

ARCHITECTURAL STYLE OF HOUSES

The architectural style of a house refers to its exterior appearance or design. Houses which have a particular architectural style can be divided into two broad classifications: the traditional styles and the contemporary styles. Fig. 11-1, shows

two popular traditional styles and two contemporary styles.

TRADITIONAL HOUSES

The traditional styles had their beginning in certain historical periods of various countries. Each style has been influenced by the backgrounds of the people of the country in which the style originated, by the climatic conditions which had to be considered in building, and finally by the materials available. Some examples of traditional styles found in the United States are discussed here to help you in identifying some basic types.

The Elizabethan, one of the many styles of English influence, is a one and one-half to a two-story structure with steep sloping gable roof, Fig. 11-2; frequently having dormer windows; large chimney; and an exterior of brick, stone, or stucco with half-timber construction.

The Georgian style house is a two-story house characterized by well-balanced and well-proportioned masses in the exterior walls with many classic details, and chimneys, and a hip roof. The siding may be brick, stone, or wood.

Spanish architecture features a one or a two-story house with a red-tile, low pitched roof; light colored stucco walls; and a patio (pa'ti-o), which lends itself to outdoor living. Spanish architecture is prevalent in the Southwest.

The Dutch Colonial is a conservative compact house of one and one-half, two, or two and one-half stories. The second story frequently projects out over the first story, and the roof is of the gambrel type. The chimney is at the end. The exterior walls may be wood or stone, and they frequently are stone on the first story with wood above.

The Cape Cod is a one or one and one-half story house of traditional design, that is still popular today. It usually has a center chimney, steep gable roof with dormers (if a story and a half) and the exterior siding is usually wood such as clapboard or shingles. The windows of the Cape Cod house have small panes typical of colonial architecture and are flanked with shutters.

CONTEMPORARY HOUSES

The term "contemporary" in house architecture is limited to the ranch style house, the multi-level house, and the modern house. However, some traditional houses have been given a modern touch, and these houses are also classified as contemporary. The design of contemporary houses has been influenced by new building materials such as plywoods, plastics, and metals; they have been influenced also by today's casual, out-of-doors living.

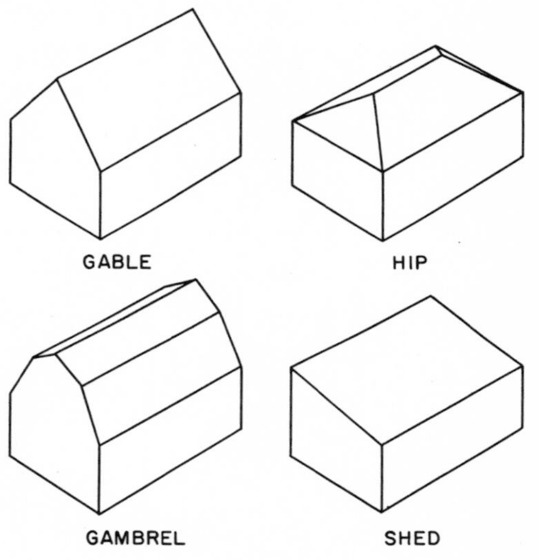

Fig. 11-2. Types of roofs.

There are certain characteristics which accompany most contemporary houses. These are: open-type, rambling floor plan with dining and living rooms combined; a utility room instead of a basement; the use of large glass areas--sometimes an entire wall will be glass, the lack of ornamentation on exterior walls, although

these walls may consist of two or more materials such as wood, brick, or stone; and a low-pitched or flat roof.

The Ranch house is a one-story structure with a low-pitched hip or gable roof, a rambling floor plan, and overhanging eaves. This is a very popular style of architecture today.

The Multi-level house, frequently called a split-level house, consists of levels which are offset from each other by a few steps or as much as one-half story. The kitchen, dining room, and living room are generally grouped on one level; the bedrooms, baths, and storage closets on another level which is usually the highest level being over the garage or recreation room.

The Modern house, may be a one-story, a two-story, or a multi-level dwelling, which features a flat or shed type (single pitch) roof, and large glass sections in exterior walls.

DESIRABLE ARCHITECTURAL FEATURES

Regardless of the style of house you choose, there are certain desirable features which you should consider when planning a house. These are:

(1) A protected or recessed entrance.
(2) An entrance hall that leads to the main areas of the house--living room, kitchen, and bedrooms without using the living room as the traffic way.
(3) A kitchen which provides ample cab-

Fig. 11-3. Floor plan of a house.

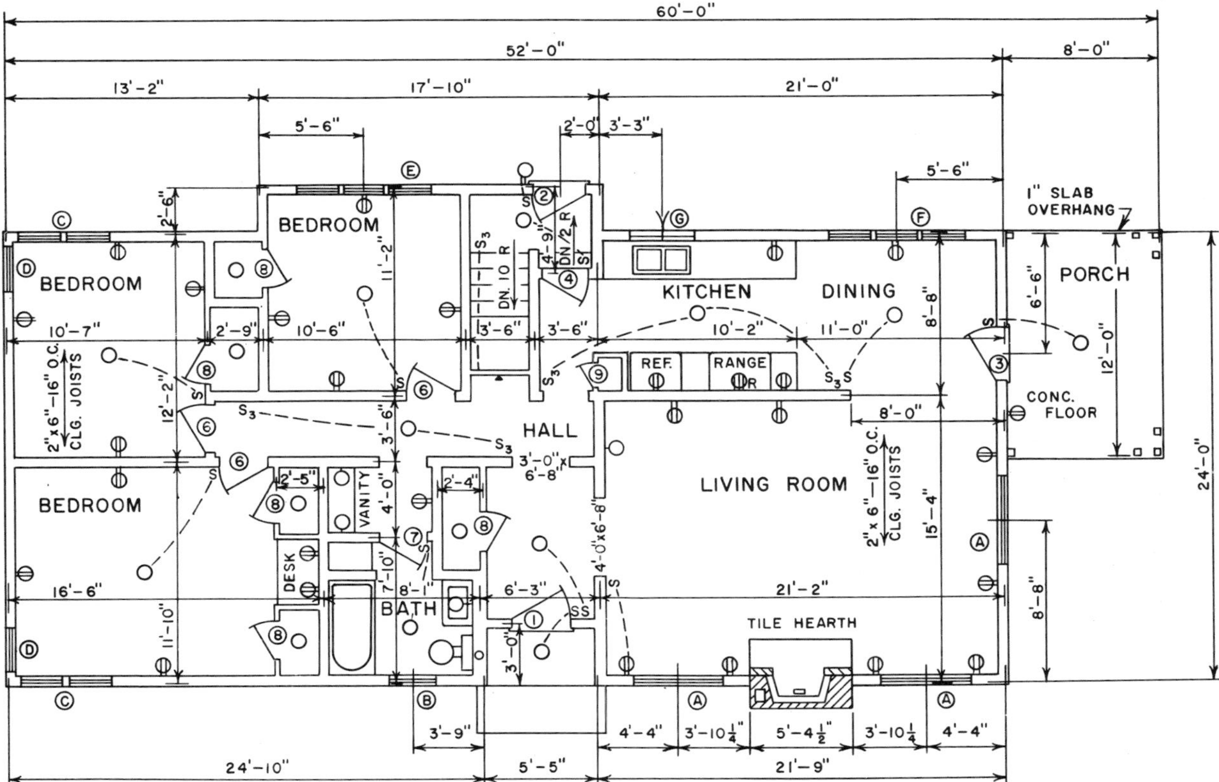

FLOOR PLAN

inet space with convenient distances between work areas.
(4) A family or recreation room with fireplace.
(5) Closet space for the entrance hall and each bedroom (two for the master bedroom).
(6) Storage space for seasonal household articles, tools, and yard and garden equipment.

TYPES OF ARCHITECTURAL DRAWINGS

The architect makes use of several types of drawings in preparing the plans for the design and construction of a house. One of the first drawings he will make is the Floor Plan (arrangement of rooms), Fig. 11-3. The floor plan contains most of the dimensions necessary in the construction of a house. It contains over-all size; location of walls, windows, doors, stairs, and electrical and plumbing details.

Once the owner is pleased with the floor plan and a style of architecture is decided upon, the architect starts to work on the Elevations, Fig. 11-4. Elevations are the exterior views of the walls--front, right-side, rear, and left-side. These are sometimes referred to as the North Elevation, East Elevation, etc., meaning the direction which the elevation faces. The elevations show the windows, doors, trim, and other details as they appear in the exterior.

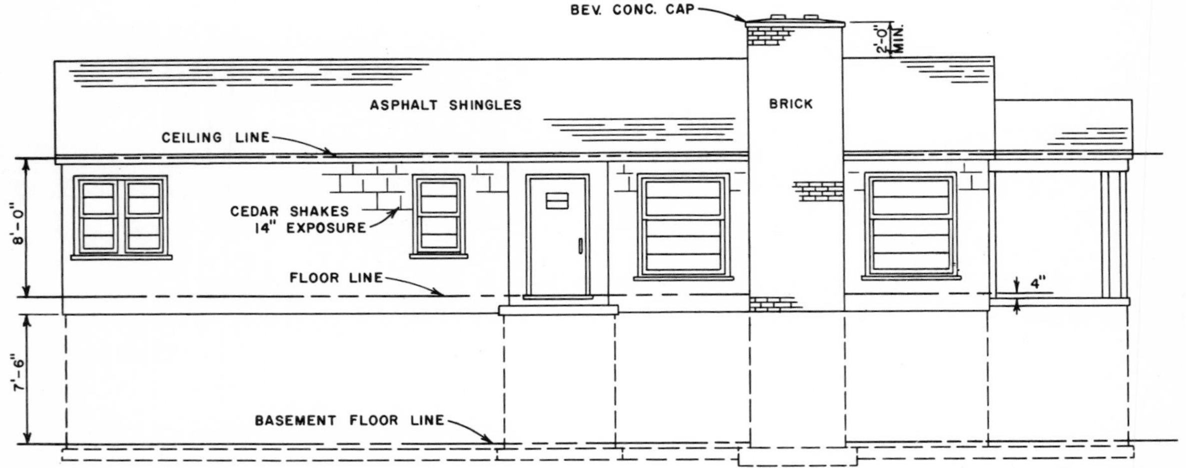

Fig. 11-4. A front elevation.

In addition to the floor plan and elevations, Detail Drawings of wall sections, fireplaces, etc., are made to show construction details, Fig. 11-5. These drawings are useful to the construction workers who build the house. The detail drawings also assure that construction will be done in a manner specified by the architect.

DRAFTY SAYS: "Do not slide instruments over drawing--lift to move."

Another type of drawing is the Perspective which is a pictorial view of the house to give the home owner a better under-

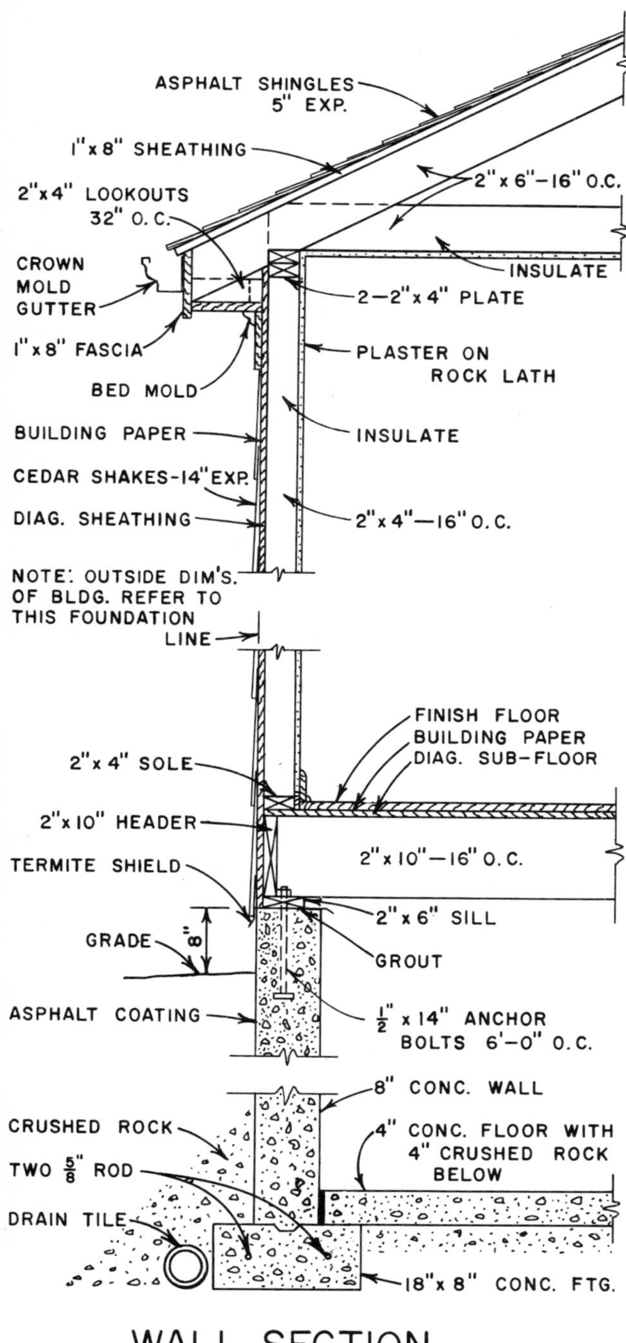

Fig. 11-5. Detail drawing of a wall section.

standing of how the house will look when completed. When perspective drawings have been given an artistic touch to include trees and shrubs, they are known as Renderings, Fig. 11-6. To give the home owner an even more realistic view of the house, a scale model is sometimes prepared, Fig. 11-7.

ARRANGEMENT OF VIEWS

Unlike the views in orthographic projection, architectural views have more flexibility in their arrangement.

Fig. 11-6. A perspective rendering.

All of the architectural views may be drawn on one sheet, but more likely several sheets will be required.

Let's see how well you can apply your knowledge of drafting to reading the architectural drawing in the next drafting activity.

Fig. 11-7. A scale model.

DRAFTING ACTIVITY

Refer to Fig. 11-3 and answer the following questions:

1. What are the over-all dimensions of the house including the porch?
2. How much does the back bedroom extend beyond the corner bedroom?

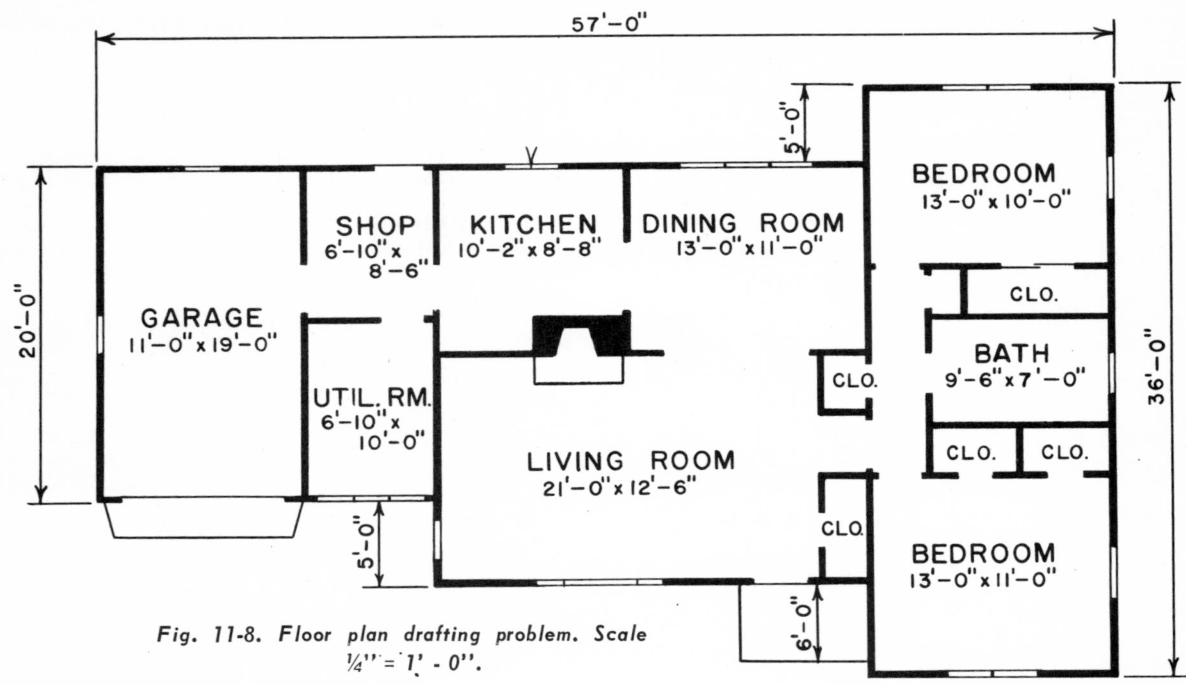

Fig. 11-8. Floor plan drafting problem. Scale ¼" = 1' - 0".

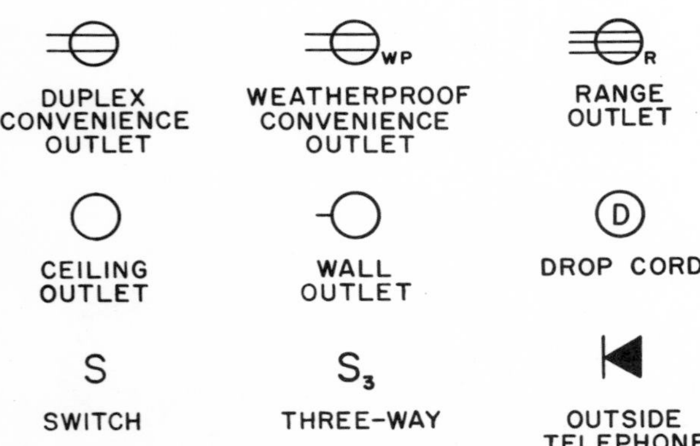

Fig. 11-9. Electrical symbols for floor plans.

DRAFTING ACTIVITY

1. Draw a floor plan of the house shown in Fig. 11-8. The interior dimensions shown are approximate room sizes and do not include wall thicknesses.
2. Include electrical, plumbing, and kitchen equipment on your floor plan. Refer to Fig. 11-9 and 11-10 for details of these.
3. Dimension the drawing in the manner shown in Fig. 11-3.

QUIZ - UNIT 11

1. What three things are required in the planning of a house?
2. What are specifications?
3. What are the various roof types?
4. All house styles may be grouped into what two broad classifications? What styles can you name under each classification?
3. Allowing 6 in. for wall thickness, what are the dimensions of the living room? Bedrooms?
4. What is the width of the kitchen?
5. What is the width of the bedroom hall? Front hall? Stairwell?
6. How many duplex convenience outlets are required? Ceiling outlets? Wall outlets? Single-pole switches? Three-way switches?

5. Name some desirable features which should be considered when planning a house?
6. What types of drawings are used in architectural drafting? What is the purpose of each?
7. What symbols are used for the following: (A) ceiling outlets, (B) wall outlets, (C) duplex convenience outlets, and (D) switches?

NEW WORDS FOR YOU TO USE

1. Specification (spes-i-fi-ka'shun)
2. Traditional (tra-dish'un-al)
3. Contemporary (kon-tem'po-rer-i)
4. Pitch (pich)
5. Eaves(evz)
6. Renderings (ren'der-ings)
7. Gambrel (gam'brel)
8. Shakes (shaks)

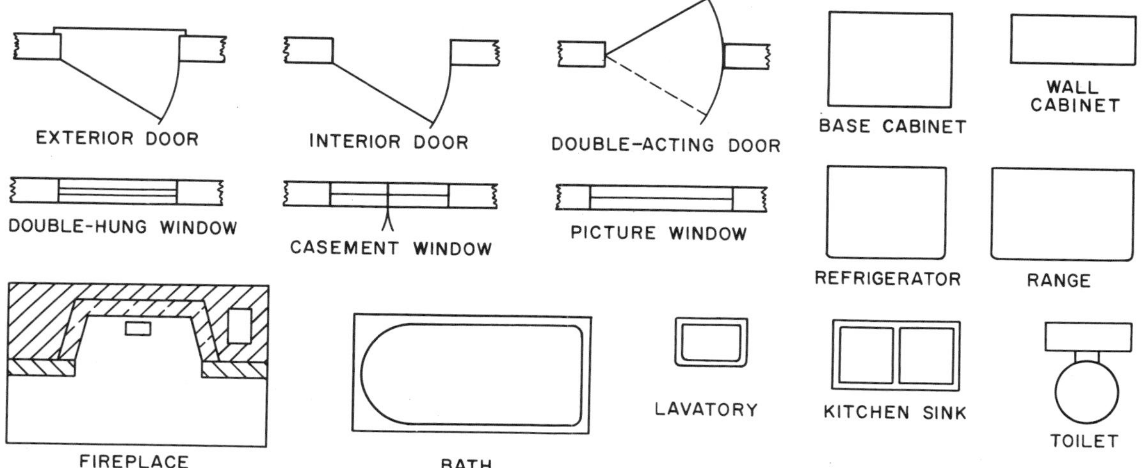

Fig. 11-10. Door, window, cabinet, plumbing, and fireplace symbols.

Monticello, home of Thomas Jefferson, near Charlottesville, Va., designed and built by Jefferson, an architect, statesman, and President of the United States. (Virginia Chamber of Commerce)

GRAPHS AND CHARTS

1. **What are graphs and charts?**
2. **How are these constructed?**
3. **What advantages do graphs and charts offer?**

Your drafting ability will be useful to you in many ways. One of these will be in making graphs and charts for work in other classes.

Graphs and charts refer to a type of drawing used by newspapers, magazines, schools, and businesses to make factual information more understandable. You will want to learn how these are constructed so that you can use this type of drafting in your school classes.

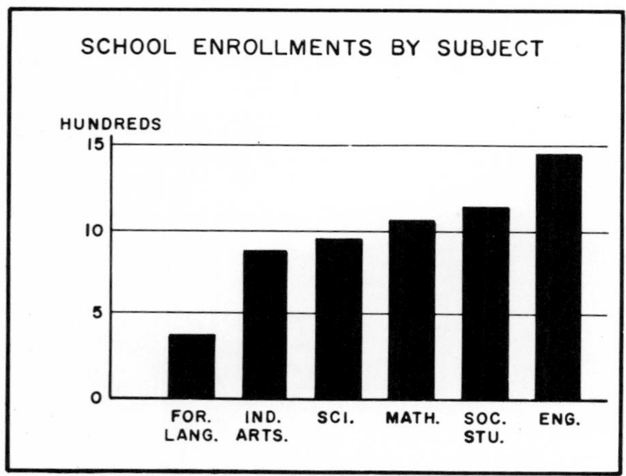

Fig. 12-1. A vertical bar graph.

You will have an opportunity in this unit to draw three types of graphs: bar, line, and pie. An introduction to charts will also be made.

BAR GRAPHS

Bar graphs are used in making comparisons, such as school enrollments, Fig. 12-1. The items to be compared are represented by "bars" which extend on a scale of values.

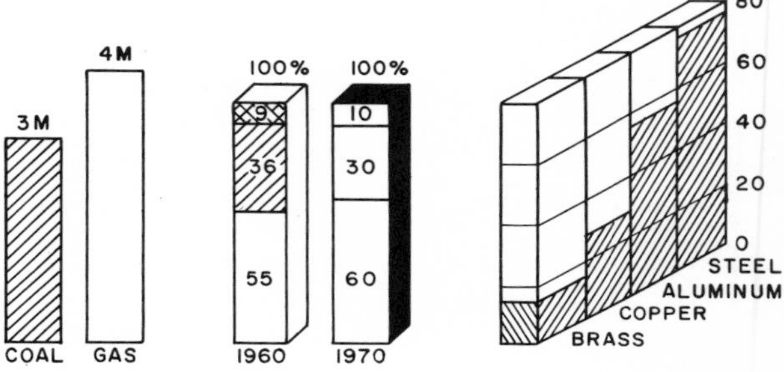

Fig. 12-2. Types of bars for graphs.

There are several ways in which bar graphs may be drawn, Fig. 12-2. Bars may be drawn either in a vertical or a horizontal position. Color may also be used for variety and emphasis.

To draw a bar graph, follow these steps:

1. Use cross section paper or plain paper.
2. Decide on horizontal or vertical graph. If the number of items to be shown is large, it is advisable to use the horizontal, Fig. 12-3. Otherwise, use the vertical graph, Fig. 12-1.
3. Figure size of rectangle into which the graph will fit. The number of bars, the space between, and the height, or scale, will need to be figured. The width of the bars and the space between them can be any reasonable width. Enough space should be

provided to label each bar. The height or scale can be any reasonable distance. The height should extend to include the largest item in the graph. Show the scale in units, fives, tens, hundreds, etc., Fig. 12-1. Try to work out a rectangle of pleasing proportion.

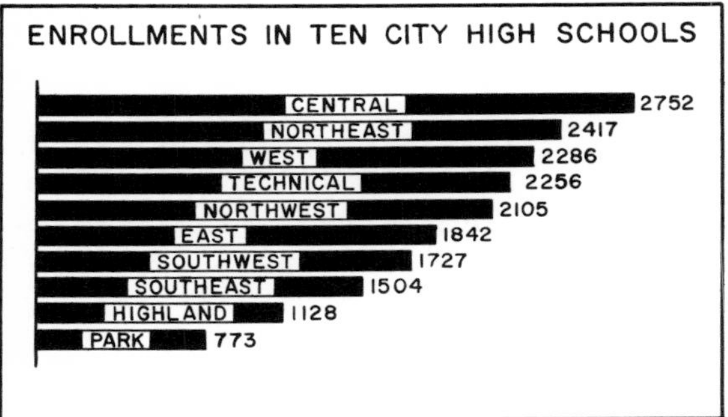

Fig. 12-3. A horizontal bar graph.

4. Draw the bars, starting with the smallest and progress to the largest.
5. Label each bar and add necessary titles and codes.
6. Shade, fill, or color the bars.
7. Draw a border around graph if desired.

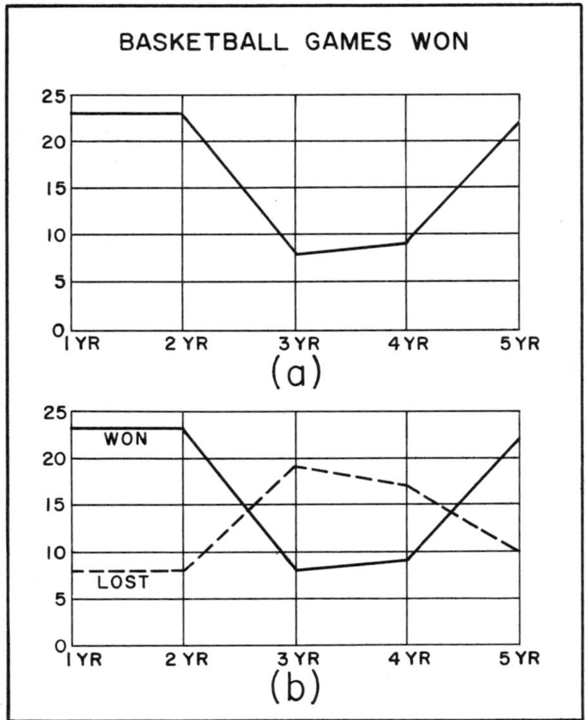

Fig. 12-4. Line graphs.

DRAFTING ACTIVITY

1. Use the following data (or data of your own), and draw a bar graph.
2. Data: Scores of high point men in basketball.

Year	
_____	- 749
_____	- 529
_____	- 648
_____	- 218
_____	- 484

LINE GRAPHS

To show the increase or decrease in something over a period of time, the line graph is often the most effective. The line graph in Fig. 12-4a, shows the number of basketball games won by a school over a period of 5 years. Fig. 12-4b provides even more information by using 2 lines in the graph to show games won and games lost. When more than one line is used the lines differ in structure. Color may also be used to contrast the lines.

DRAFTY SAYS: "Keep your hands clean."

Two factors are shown in a line graph. One of these factors is held constant (does not change) for example, a period of time-- a month or a year, and is laid off on the "x" (horizontal) axis. The other factor is variable (changes) for example, the num-

ber of games won or lost, and is laid off on the "y" (vertical) axis.

To construct a line graph, follow this procedure:

1. Figure size of rectangle needed to "frame" line graph. Find out how many divisions will be needed along the x and y axes and how much space should be provided each.
2. Make a freehand sketch of the graph showing layout of x and y axes.
3. Locate and draw rectangle for graph on cross sectioned or plain paper.
4. Lay out scale on x and y axes and draw grid (cross section) lines if plain paper is used.
5. Plot data.
6. Connect these points with a line.
7. Label the graph with title, necessary notes, and codes.

DRAFTING ACTIVITY

1. Use the following data (or data of your own) and draw a line graph.
2. Data: Enrollment in Central High School for 5 years.

Year	
____	- 416
____	- 428
____	- 509
____	- 637
____	- 814

PIE OR CIRCLE GRAPHS

When the information you want to show represents 100%, or the whole, you will find the pie graph most useful. This type of graph is called a pie graph because the sections resemble pieces of pie. Such a graph enables a person to quickly observe how each part compares with the whole. The rank achieved in scouting by 60 boys attending a scout camp is shown in Fig. 12-5.

The sections of a pie graph may be left plain, cross hatched, or colored for contrast.

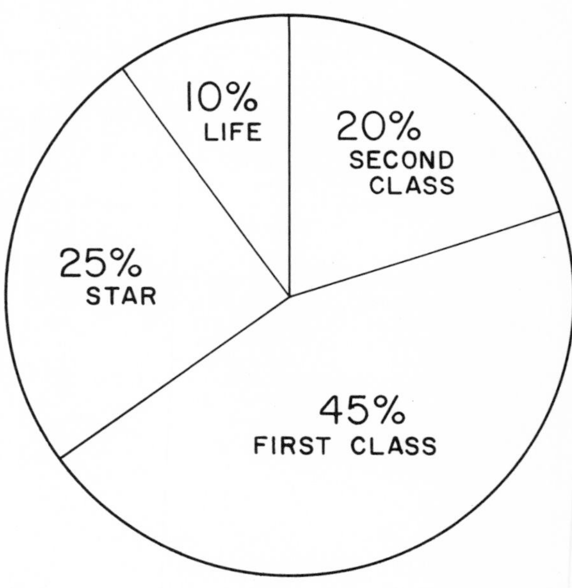

Fig. 12-5. A pie graph.

To construct a pie graph, follow this procedure:

1. Determine the size of the graph, based on space available and amount of information to be lettered within the sections.
2. Draw the circle.
3. Figure size of sections. The whole circle equals 100%; it also equals 360°. Therefore,

$$1\% = \frac{360}{100} = 3.6^{\circ}.$$

4. Start at any convenient place on the circle, usually at the top, and with the aid of a protractor, lay off each section.
5. Letter notes for each section, horizontally if possible, within the graph. When space is limited, letter outside the graph and extend a leader to the graph section.
6. Letter the title of the graph.

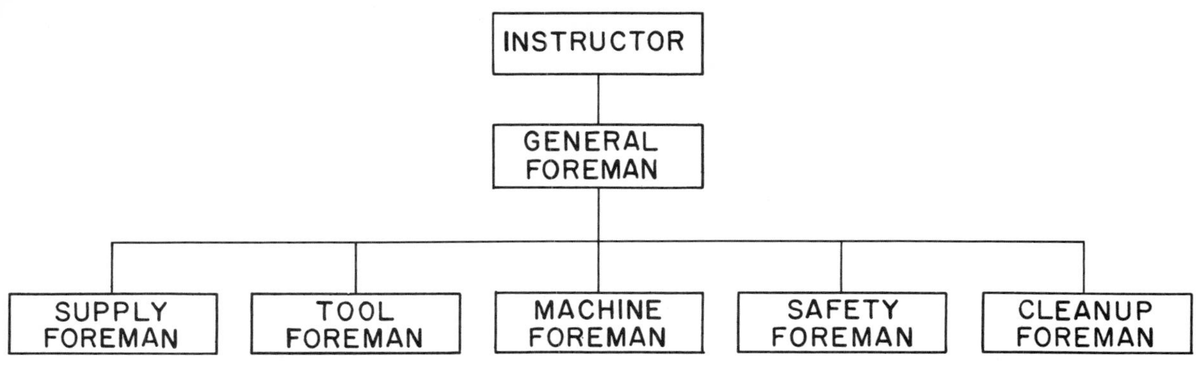

Fig. 12-6. An organizational chart showing a school shop personnel organization.

DRAFTING ACTIVITY

1. Use the following data (or data of your own) and draw a pie graph.
2. Data: Enrollment in a high school by classes:

seniors	150
juniors	225
sophomores	300
freshmen	325

CHARTS

Charts, like graphs, are prepared to simplify the presentation of certain information, or to clarify a complicated process. Two types of charts which are commonly used are the organizational chart, Fig. 12-6, and the flow chart, Fig. 12-7. These charts may be drawn to any size appropriate for the information presented and the space available.

QUIZ - UNIT 12

1. What purpose do graphs serve?
2. What types of graphs are discussed in this unit?
3. Can you name and describe other graphs?
4. When would you use the horizontal bar graph rather than the vertical?
5. What determines the size of the rectangle "framing" a bar graph?
6. If you wanted to compare two items over a period of time which type graph would you use?
7. What is the best type of graph to use in illustrating how you spend a 24 hour day?
8. What is the purpose of an organizational chart? A flow chart?

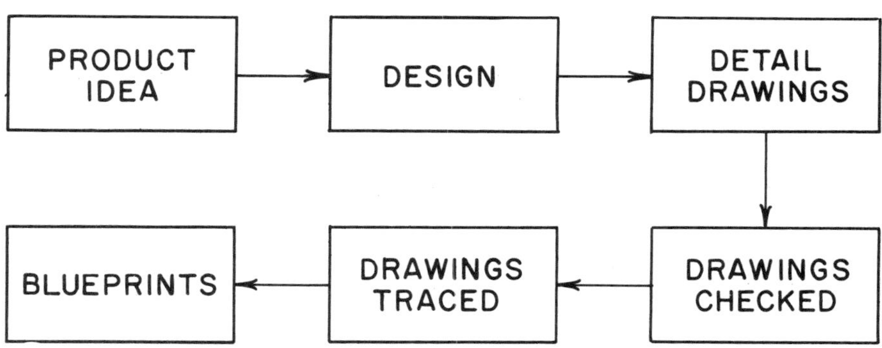

Fig. 12-7. Flow chart showing product development from idea to blueprint.

AERIAL PHOTOGRAPH USED IN THE PREPARATION OF MAP SHOWN BELOW

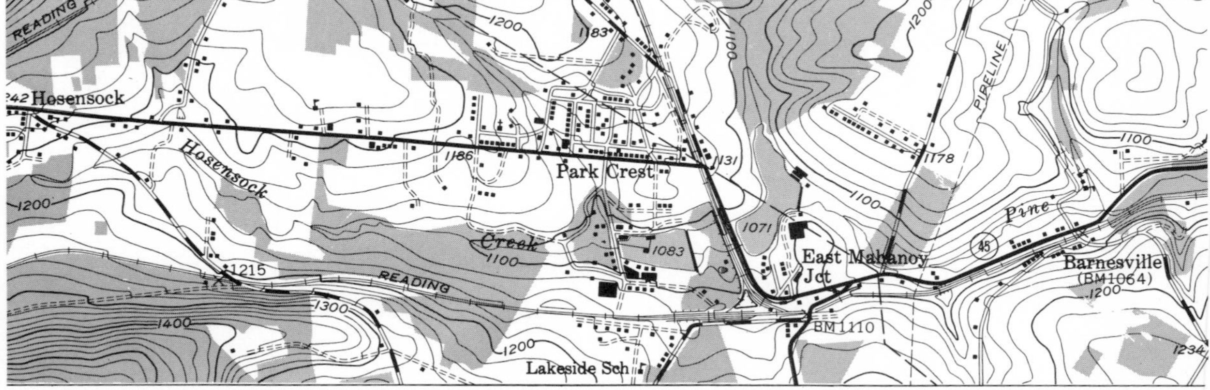

Fig. 13-1. Aerial photography is used in map making.
(U. S. Geological Survey)

MAP DRAFTING

1. **How are maps drawn?**
2. **What kinds of maps are there?**
3. **What do maps tell you?**

Perhaps you have made a long trip by auto or by plane, hiked cross-country, or camped out. If you have, then you already know something about maps. This unit will help you understand the draftsman's part in the making of maps.

Maps are one-view drawings known as topographical drawings, and are used to describe a portion of or all of the earth's surface. Topography means the shape of the land's surface including its hills, valleys, streams, lakes, and trees. Frequently topographical maps show roads, cities, etc. Maps are drawn by topographical draftsmen who work from data gathered in the field by civil engineers and surveyors. The use of aerial photographs is reducing the amount of field work necessary, Fig. 13-1. A surveying crew gathering

data for a new road construction project is shown in Fig. 13-2. A map will be drawn before construction starts.

Travelers over America's highways depend upon road maps for direction to get to their destinations. Outdoorsmen depend upon maps to guide them in strange territories. Architects and engineers need maps describing the shape of the land and the sub-soil to properly plan buildings and highways. A person building a house needs

Fig. 13-2. Surveying crew at work. (Michigan Highway Dept.)

an accurate map of the boundaries of his lot in order to properly locate the house.

SCALE AND DIRECTION OF MAPS

Maps, like many other objects, are drawn to scale. This scale may range from 1 in. equaling a few feet to 1 in. equaling several hundred miles. North on a map is assumed to be at the top of the map unless otherwise indicated by an arrow. Following are descriptions of maps which are used by all of us.

GEOGRAPHIC MAPS

This map is the type found in your geography books and shows the earth's physical features--both natural and man made. The geographic map usually represents large areas and only the principal mountains, streams, lakes, cities, roads, etc. are shown. Smaller areas may be shown also on a geographic map and on such maps all or nearly all of the physical features of an area may be shown.

CONTOUR MAPS

A map which shows the variation in elevations of the land by lines connecting points of the same elevation is called a contour map, Fig. 13-3. Imaginary lines

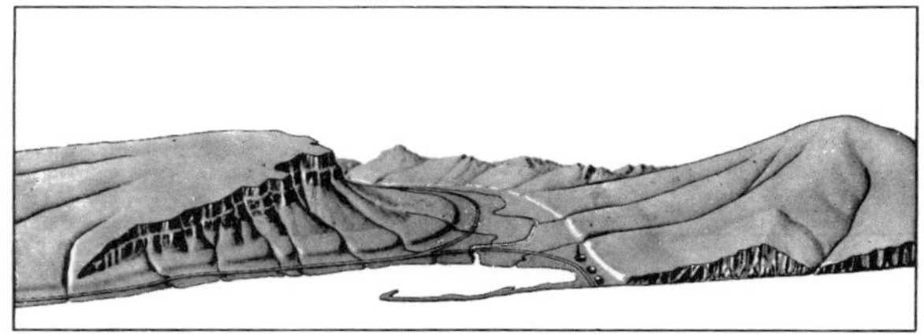

Fig. 13-3. A contour map. (U. S. Geological Survey)

on the earth's surface (as if the earth had been sliced horizontally at uniform heights) are drawn on the map to represent the slope or shape of the land, Fig. 13-4. The vertical difference between contours may range from less than a foot on small maps to over 200 ft. on larger maps. When the contours are close together, the surface is steep; when they are far apart, the slope is less steep. The contours are numbered to indicate elevation in feet from some fixed elevation such as sea level.

Contour maps are necessary in the initial planning of buildings, highways, airfields, and other construction projects.

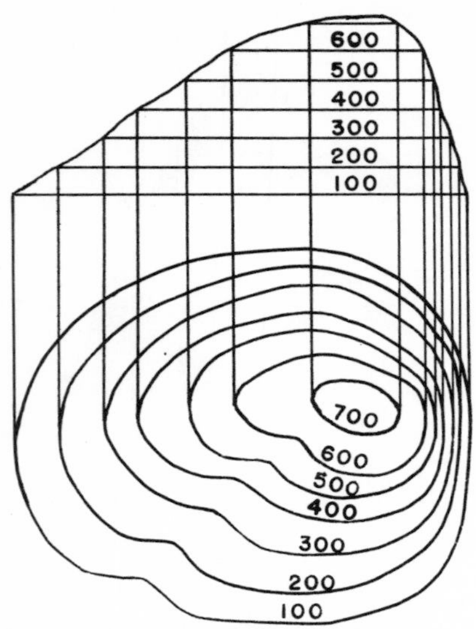

Fig. 13-4. Drawing contour lines.

PLAT MAPS

A plat (or plot) is the map of a small piece of ground such as a building site for a house, school or camp, Fig. 13-5. If your parents own their own house, they may have a plat of their lot showing the boundary lines of the property and the location of the house upon the lot.

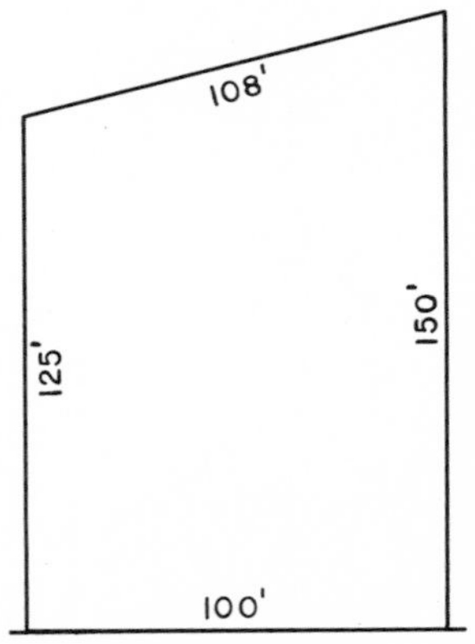

Fig. 13-5. A plat map.

Road maps direct us to many interesting places. Shown below is the new Paseo Bridge across the Missouri River, Kansas City, Mo. (Massie – Missouri Resources Div.)

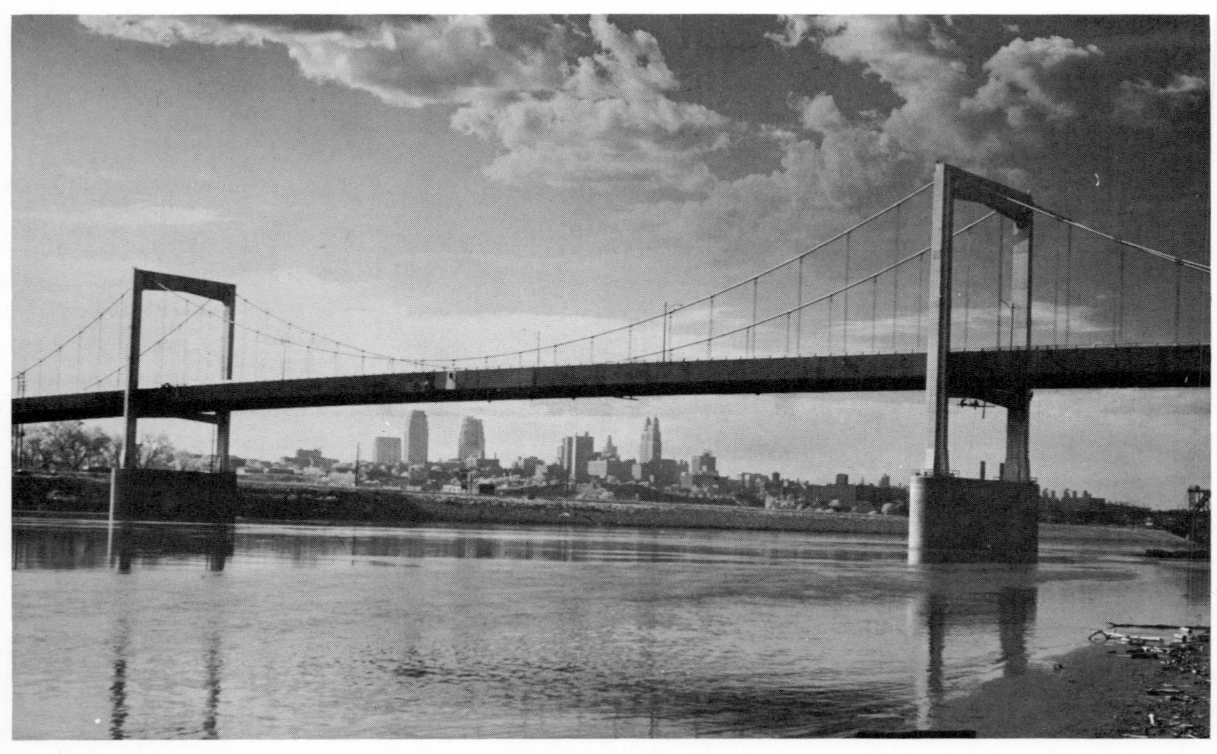

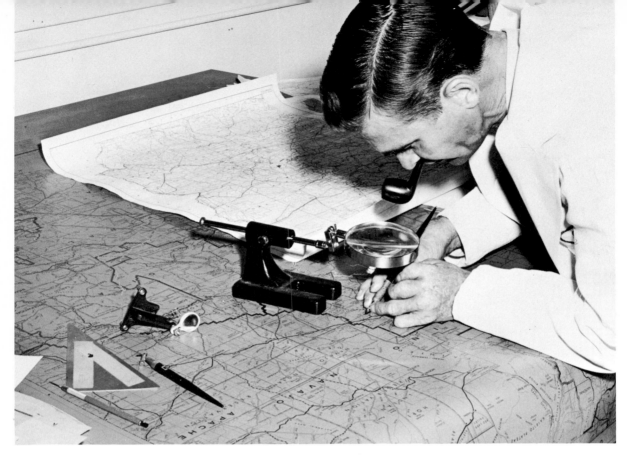

Fig. 13-6. Draftsman at work on a highway map. (Arizona Highway Dept.)

ROAD MAPS

State highway maps are available for every state in the union showing inter-state, state, and county roads. In addition, the map shows types of road surfaces, cities, towns, distances between points, a scale of miles, state parks, and other points of interest. Data for these maps are gathered by state highway surveying crews and are continually being revised and brought up-to-date by map draftsmen, Fig. 13-6.

Street maps for the principal cities of the state are usually shown around the edge of the state map. Highways, through and around the cities, are shown as well as the main streets of the city.

PICTORIAL MAPS

Pictorial maps are issued by cities, governmental agencies, civic organizations, and tourist agencies to provide an over-view of an area showing principal points of interest, Fig. 13-7. You will observe that pictorial drawing has been used in the making of these maps. The chief purpose of these maps is to provide a "birds-eye-view" of an area, so that a stranger may readily see the location of certain buildings and points of interest. While these maps may not be as accurate in detail as some of the maps discussed

DRAFTY SAYS: "When erasing, use a shield to protect nearby lines."

previously, they are an effective means of giving directions.

MAP READING ACTIVITY

1. From a highway map of your state, plan a trip to another city within your state and to a third city and return.
2. Figure the mileage for this trip.
3. Write out the directions for someone else to follow this same route.

DRAFTING ACTIVITY

Draw one of the following maps showing prominent places and streets or roads. Use an appropriate scale. The map should be neatly drawn, and should be easily understood by another person expecting to follow it.

1. Your route from home to school.
2. Your paper route.

QUIZ - UNIT 13

1. Maps are the result of the work of several individuals. Who are these persons and what part does each perform in map making?
2. What features are shown on topographical maps?
3. What is a geographic map and how is it used?
4. Contour maps are used for what purpose? How do they differ from other maps?
5. What is the plat map and when is it used?
6. How do pictorial maps differ from other types of maps? What is the principal use of these maps?

NEW WORDS FOR YOU TO USE

1. Contour (kon'toor)
2. Surveying (ser-va'ing)
3. Topographical (top-o-graf'i-kal)

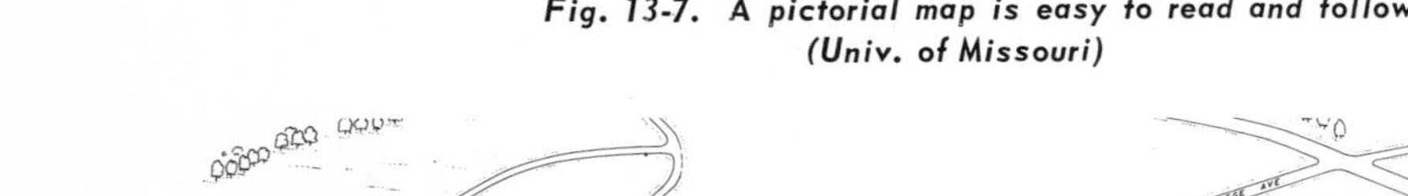

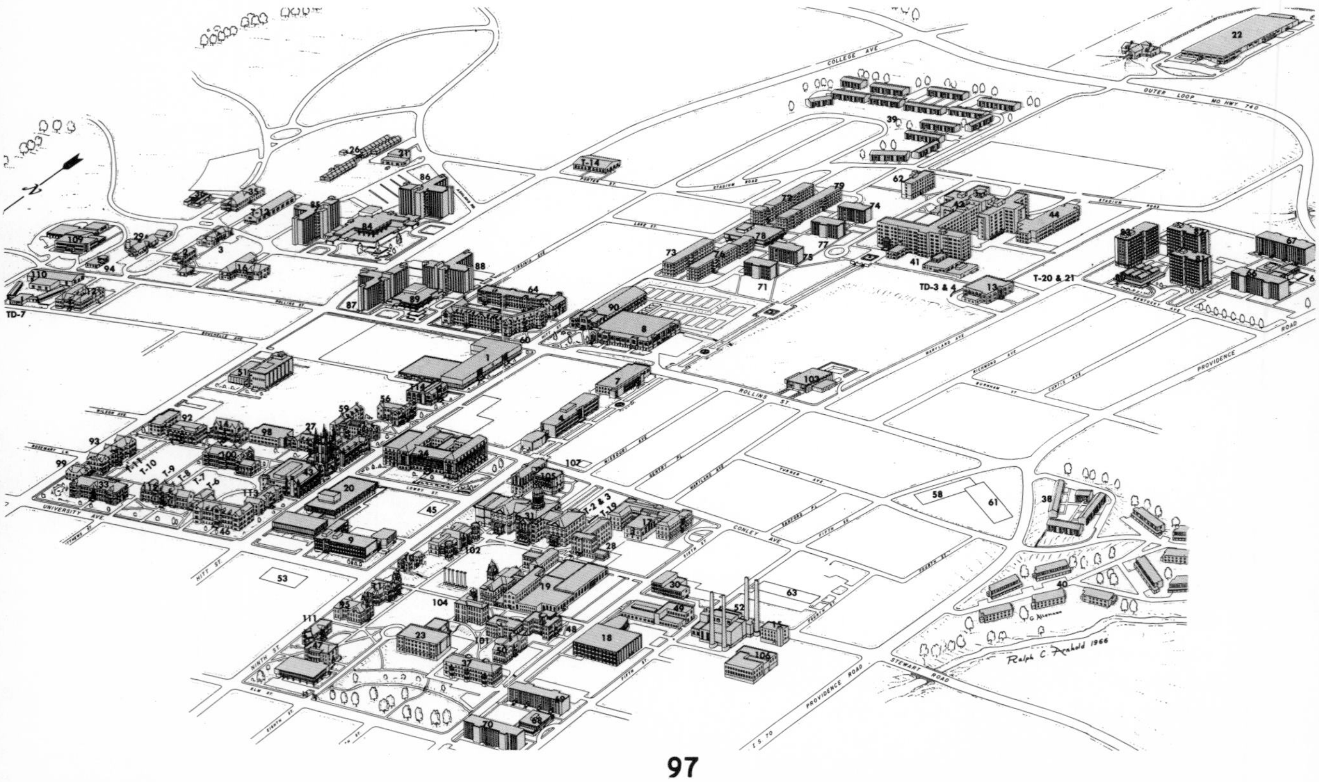

Fig. 13-7. A pictorial map is easy to read and follow. (Univ. of Missouri)

Fig. 14-1. Positive print making machine in use. (Charles Bruning Co., Inc.)

MAKING AND READING BLUEPRINTS

1. **What kinds of prints are used today?**
2. **How are these prints made?**
3. **What skills are needed in reading drawings and prints?**

Drawings and blueprints are the chief means of conveying an idea for a new product to the workmen who produce it. For example, an engineer who gets an idea for an improved rocket device must make use of drafting to communicate his idea to the workmen who will build the device. This is why drafting is known as the "language of industry."

Often several copies of a drawing are needed for the various workmen on a job. It would be too expensive to supply everyone with an original drawing, so duplicates in the form of prints are made.

Such prints are often referred to as "blueprints," because the original type of print was blue with white lines. However,

in addition to blueprints, there are other types of prints called "positive prints" which have dark lines on a light background. They are in common use today in schools and industry.

In this unit, you will learn how prints are made, and you will also get some experience in reading prints.

HOW PRINTS ARE MADE

Before prints can be made, tracings of the original drawings must be made on thin transparent paper or cloth. They are called tracings, because they are laid over the original drawing and traced. More experienced draftsmen frequently make the original drawing right on tracing paper from which prints are to be made. This saves the time of tracing the drawing later.

The tracing serves the same purpose as a negative in photography. It is placed over a chemically-coated, light-sensitized paper and exposed to a strong light which produces an exact copy of the drawing. This exposure to light may be done in a sun frame or in a print making machine, Fig. 14-1, where a strong artificial light is used.

The tracing and exposed paper are then removed, the tracing saved for future use, and the print developed. The development of prints will be discussed under the types of prints which follow.

BLUEPRINTS

The blueprint is a print having white lines on a blue background. Perhaps you have seen one of these. It is the least expensive print to make; it is quite durable under continuous use; and it does not fade readily when exposed to a strong light, such as the sun. Because of the blue background, however, it is difficult to make changes or notes on the print.

Exposing the blueprint paper to light may require as little as 30 seconds to as much as 3 minutes or more depending on the brand of paper and the intensity of the light. After the blueprint paper has been exposed to the light, the chemical on the coated paper receiving the light becomes insoluble and when washed in water turns blue. The chemical beneath the lines on the tracing has not been exposed to light, and therefore dissolves in the washing process, leaving the white paper showing as white lines. The print is then hung up to dry.

After the first water bath, the intensity of the print can be increased, if desired, by washing the print in a solution of potassium dichromate (1 teaspoon to a gallon of water). This should be followed by a rinse in clear water.

POSITIVE PRINTS

Positive prints are prints with dark lines and a light background. Two processes in common use that produce positive prints are described here.

The Bruning process (black lines with white background) requires a thin liquid developer. Ammonia vapor is the developer of the Ozalid process (black, brown, blue, or red lines on a light background of white, yellow, pink, blue, or green). The light causes the chemically-coated paper to fade during exposure except under the lines of the tracing. When exposed to the developer, the area which was affected by the light, comes out white, or a pale color of the paper selected, and the unexposed chemical turns to a dark color.

Positive prints do not shrink in the developing process but remain essentially the same size. Notes or changes can readily be added on their light background. If exposed to strong light for a period of time, these prints will fade.

BLUEPRINT READING

Blueprint reading is a matter of understanding the types of drawings, lines, symbols, and notes. You have been studying these in previous units and should be able to read most of the prints in your school shop. The prints for two advanced projects, which you may have an opportunity to make--one from the text Metalworking by Boyd, and one from the text Woodworking by Wagner are shown in Fig. 14-2 and 14-3. Let's see how much information you are able to obtain concerning the size, location of parts, shape, quantity and kinds of materials used.

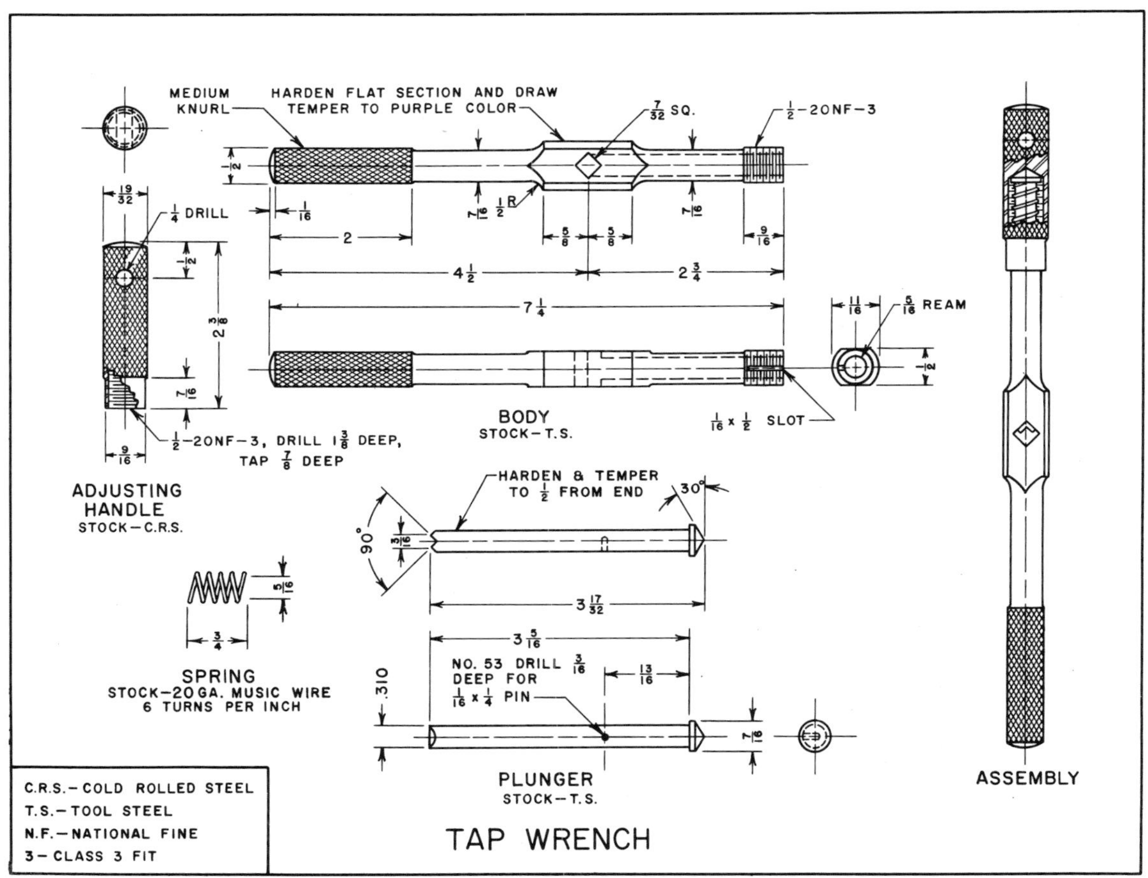

Fig. 14-2. Print of a tap wrench.

BLUEPRINT READING ACTIVITY

Study the print in Fig. 14-2 and answer the following:

1. How many separate parts are there to the tap wrench?
2. What is the diameter of the knurled part of the adjusting handle?
3. To what depth is the adjusting handle threaded? What is the size and type of thread?
4. What kind and size of stock is needed to make the tap wrench body?
5. What is the thickness of the flat

section of the body?

6. What is the size of the hole in the body which contains the plunger?
7. What is the diameter of the plunger stem? The plunger cap?
8. Describe the means by which the plunger is kept aligned in the body.
9. The spring is made from what material? What is its inside diameter?

answer the following:

1. What are the over-all width, length, and height dimensions of the coffee table?
2. What are the dimensions of the legs?
3. How are the legs fastened to the top?
4. Where are the mounting plates

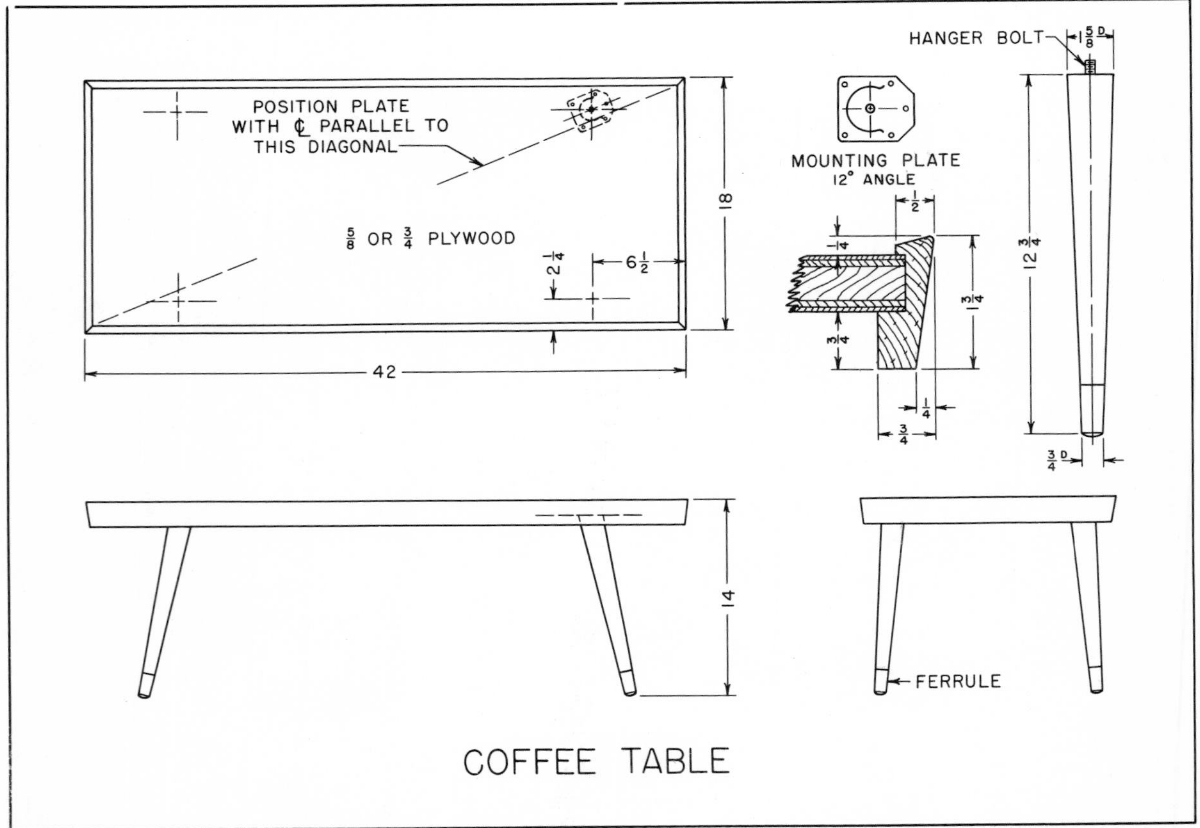

Fig. 14-3. One type of positive print showing a coffee table.

10. What parts of the tap wrench are hardened and tempered?
11. Check with your instructor on the price of materials and figure the cost of this project.

BLUEPRINT READING ACTIVITY

Study the print in Fig. 14-3 and

positioned?

5. Of what material is the top constructed?
6. What are the over-all dimensions of the side rail?
7. Other than wood screws, how many metal parts are used in constructing this table? What are they?
8. Check with your instructor on the

price of materials and figure the cost of this project.

QUIZ - UNIT 14

1. What kinds of prints are discussed in this unit? How do they differ?
2. Before prints can be made, what must be prepared? How are these prepared?
3. In what ways may prints be exposed?
4. Explain how prints are developed.
5. What are the advantages and disadvantages of blueprints? Positive prints?

NEW WORDS FOR YOU TO USE

1. Ammonia (a-mo'ni-a)
2. Dichromate (di-kro'mat)
3. Durable (dyoor'a-bel)
4. Insoluble (in-sol'u-ble)
5. Knurl (nurl)
6. Potassium (po-tas'i-um)
7. Solution (so-loo'shun)

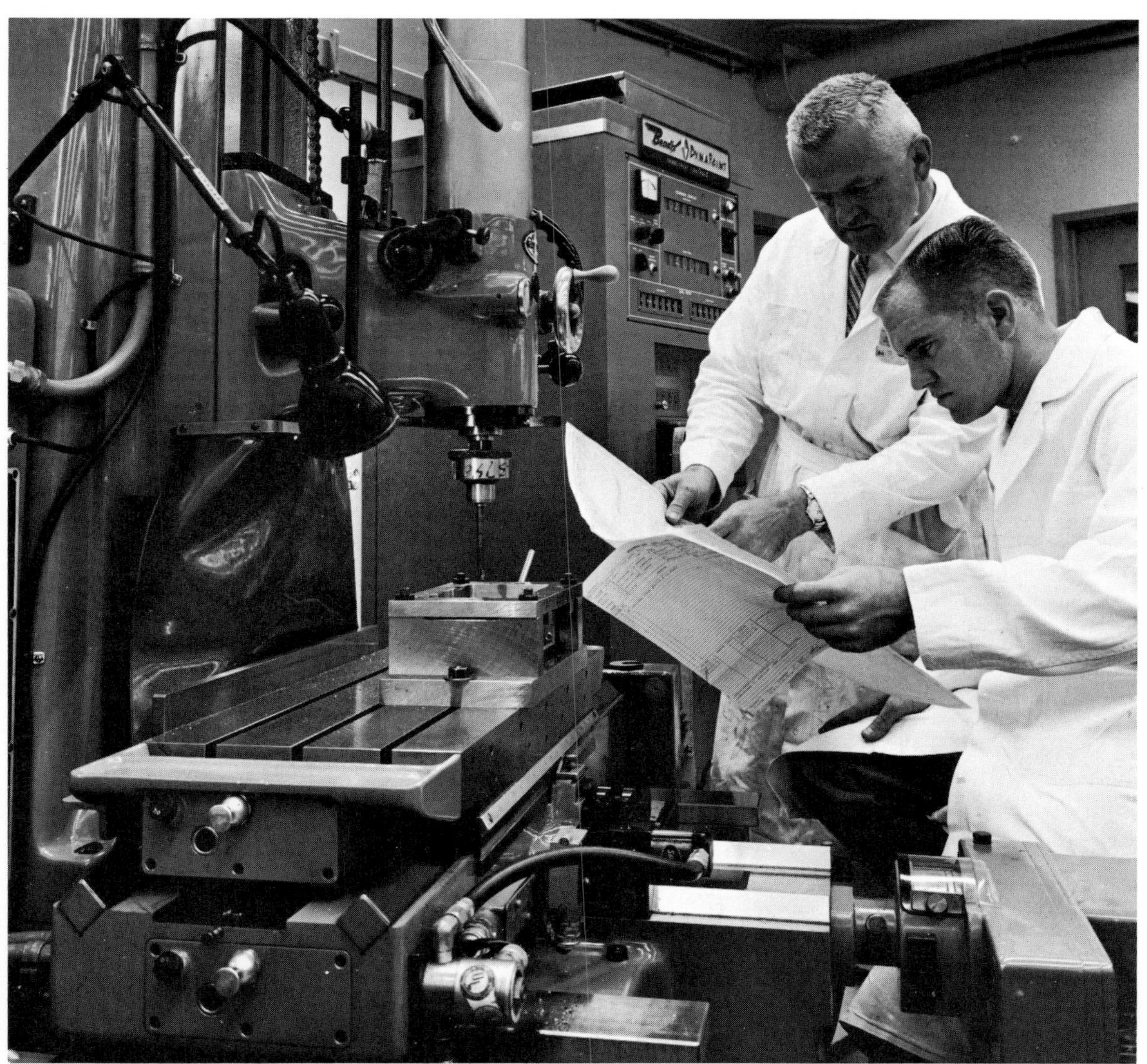

Checking a print for details.
(AiResearch Mfg. Co.)

FOR YOUR FURTHER STUDY

Coover, Shriver L., DRAWING and BLUEPRINT READING, McGraw-Hill Co., Inc.

Edgar, Ray J., GRAPHIC ARCHITECTURAL DRAFTING, McKnight & McKnight Publishing Co.

Feirer, John L., DRAWING and PLANNING for INDUSTRIAL ARTS, Chas. A. Bennett Co., Inc.

French, T. E., and Svensen, C. L., MECHANICAL DRAWING, McGraw-Hill Co.

Fryklund, V. C., and Kepler, Ray, GENERAL DRAFTING, McKnight and McKnight Publishing Co.

Giachino, J. W., and Beukema, H. J., DRAFTING, American Technical Society.

Giachino, J. W., and Beukema, H. J., EVERDAY SKETCHING & DRAFTING, American Technical Society.

Glazner, E. R., and Clark, Coly, INDUSTRIAL ARTS DRAWING, The Steck Co.

Hepler, Donald E., and Wallach, Paul, ARCHITECTURE DRAFTING and DESIGN, McGraw-Hill Co.

Scrogin, Everett, and Bettencourt, W. B., APPLIED DRAWING and DESIGNS, McKnight and McKnight Publishing Co.

Waffle, Harvey W., ARCHITECTURAL DRAWING, Bruce Publishing Co.

Walker, John R., and Plevyak, Edward, INDUSTRIAL ARTS DRAFTING, The Goodheart-Willcox Co.

ACKNOWLEDGMENT

In writing this book, the author was most fortunate in having the counsel, encouragement, and technical assistance of his colleagues at the University of Missouri. To Dr. H. H. London, Professor of Industrial Education, Mr. D. B. Doty, Assistant Professor of Industrial Arts, Dr. Wilbur R. Miller, Assistant Professor of Industrial Education, Dr. David L. Jelden, Research Associate in Industrial Education, and Mrs. Frank Roberts, Instructor in Education, he is deeply grateful.

To his wife, Elaine, and to his daughters, Barbara, Marian, and Patricia, he is greatly indebted, for without their patience, encouragement, and assistance, this book would not have been possible.

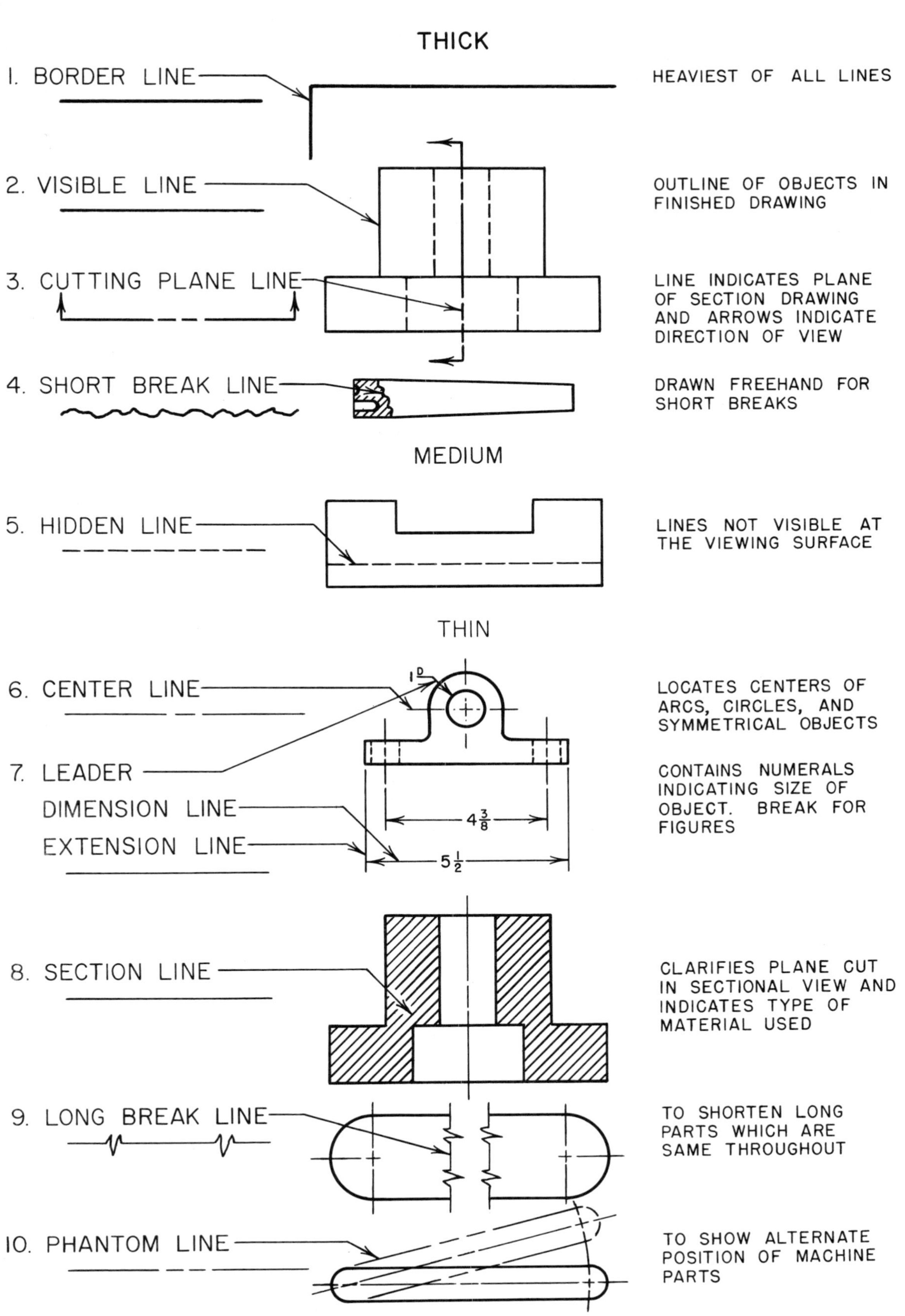
THICK
1. BORDER LINE
HEAVIEST OF ALL LINES
2. VISIBLE LINE
OUTLINE OF OBJECTS IN FINISHED DRAWING
3. CUTTING PLANE LINE
LINE INDICATES PLANE OF SECTION DRAWING AND ARROWS INDICATE DIRECTION OF VIEW
4. SHORT BREAK LINE
DRAWN FREEHAND FOR SHORT BREAKS
MEDIUM
5. HIDDEN LINE
LINES NOT VISIBLE AT THE VIEWING SURFACE
THIN
6. CENTER LINE
LOCATES CENTERS OF ARCS, CIRCLES, AND SYMMETRICAL OBJECTS
1D
7. LEADER
DIMENSION LINE
EXTENSION LINE
CONTAINS NUMERALS INDICATING SIZE OF OBJECT. BREAK FOR FIGURES
4 3/8
5 1/2
8. SECTION LINE
CLARIFIES PLANE CUT IN SECTIONAL VIEW AND INDICATES TYPE OF MATERIAL USED
9. LONG BREAK LINE
TO SHORTEN LONG PARTS WHICH ARE SAME THROUGHOUT
10. PHANTOM LINE
TO SHOW ALTERNATE POSITION OF MACHINE PARTS

Alphabet of lines.

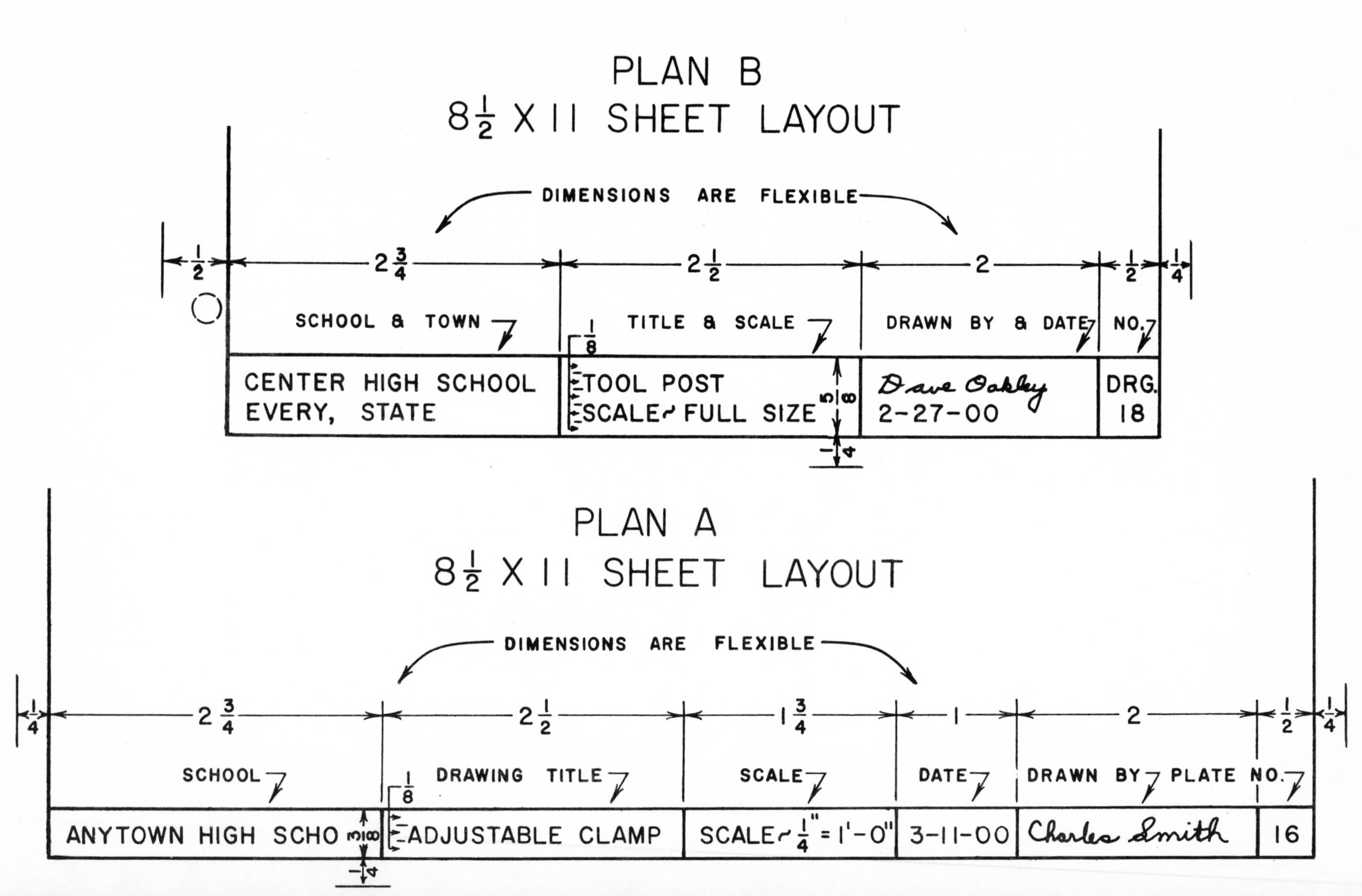
PLAN B
8½ X 11 SHEET LAYOUT
DIMENSIONS ARE FLEXIBLE
½
2¾
2½
2
½
¼
SCHOOL & TOWN
TITLE & SCALE
DRAWN BY & DATE
NO.
⅛
⅝
¼
CENTER HIGH SCHOOL
EVERY, STATE
TOOL POST
SCALE~ FULL SIZE
Dave Oakley
2-27-00
DRG.
18
PLAN A
8½ X 11 SHEET LAYOUT
DIMENSIONS ARE FLEXIBLE
¼
2¾
2½
1¾
1
2
½
¼
SCHOOL
DRAWING TITLE
SCALE
DATE
DRAWN BY
PLATE NO.
⅛
⅜
¼
ANYTOWN HIGH SCHO
ADJUSTABLE CLAMP
SCALE~ ¼" = 1'-0"
3-11-00
Charles Smith
16

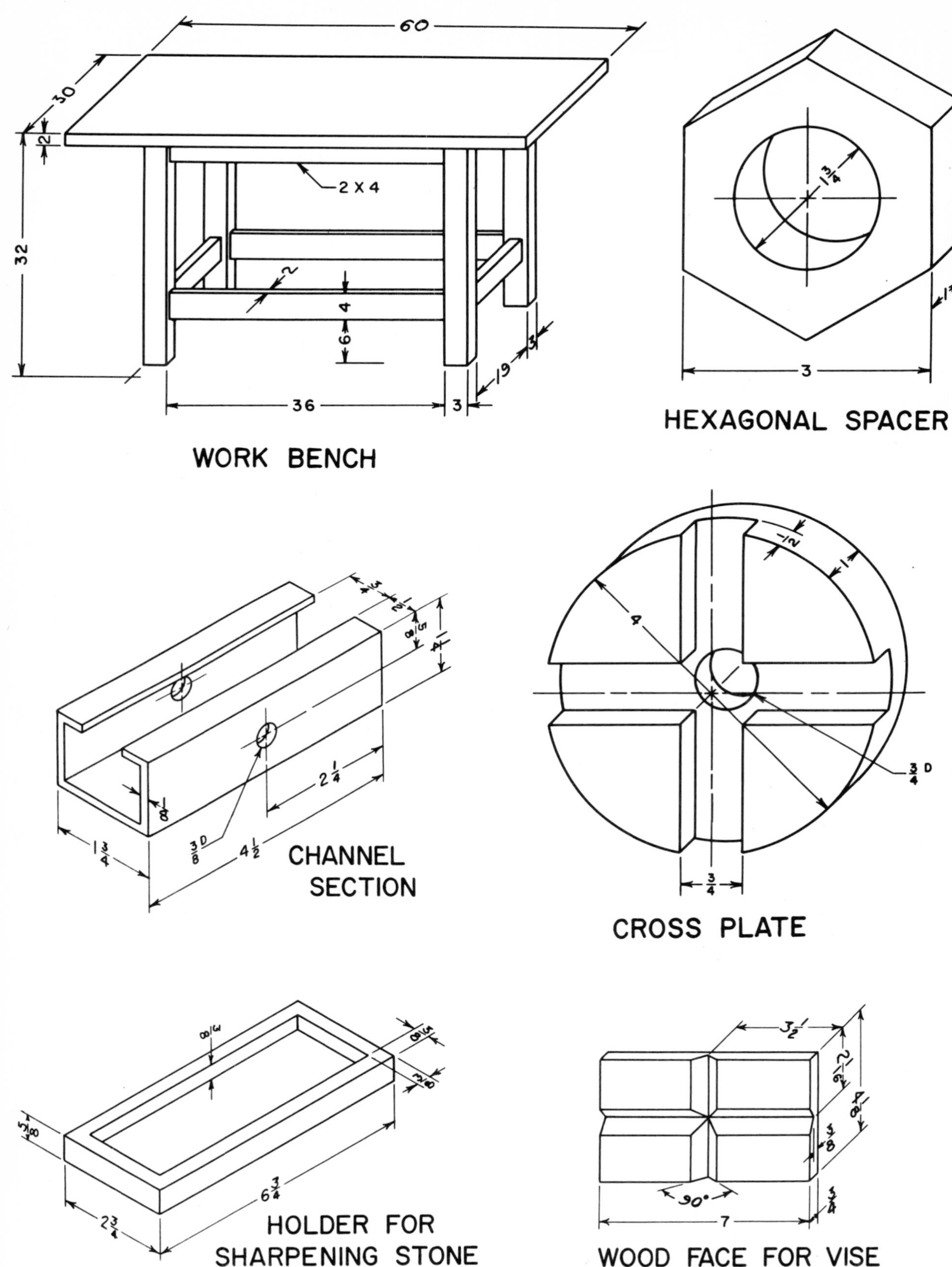

Additional drawing problems--multiview.

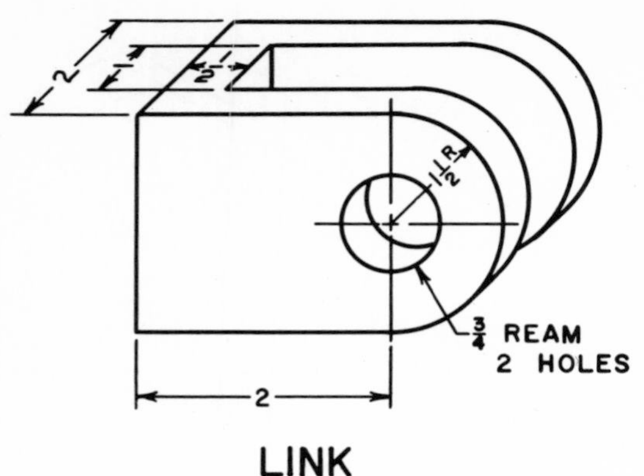

LINK

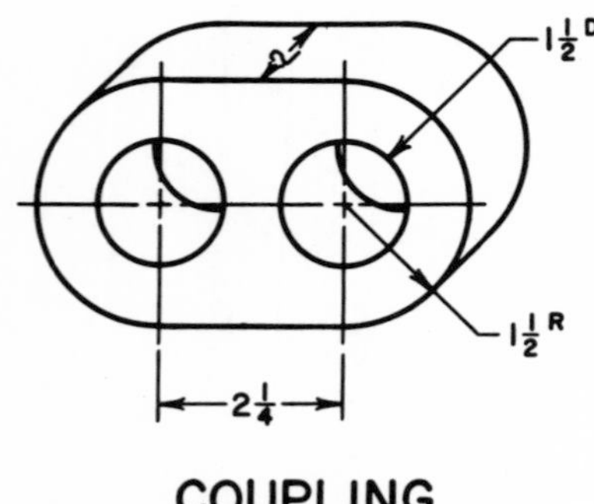

COUPLING

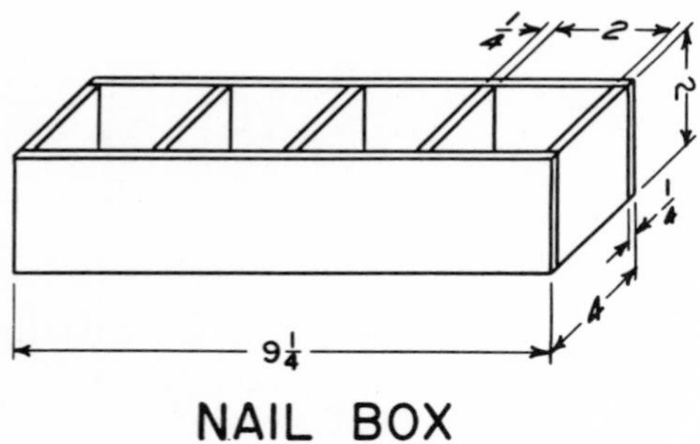

NAIL BOX

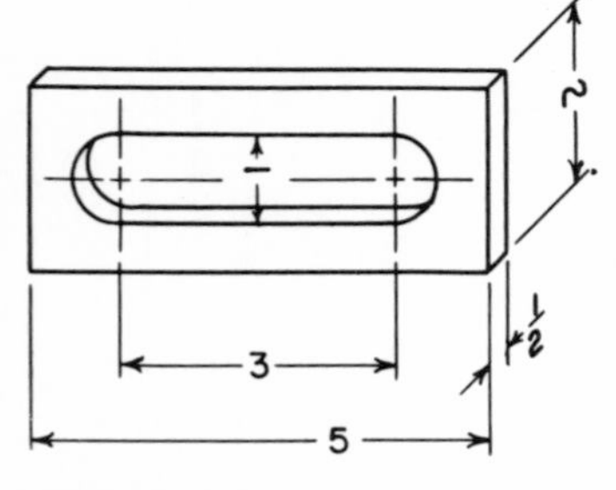

GUIDE PLATE

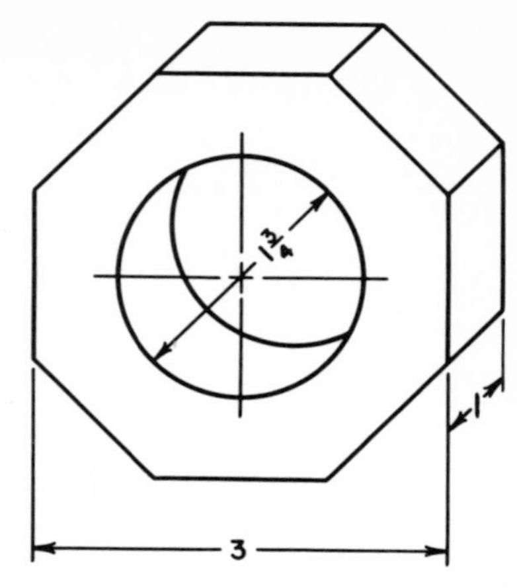

OCTAGONAL SPACER

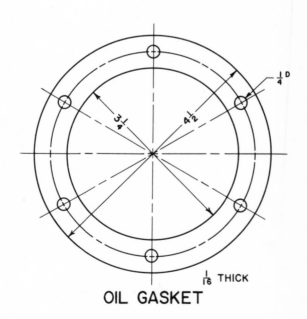

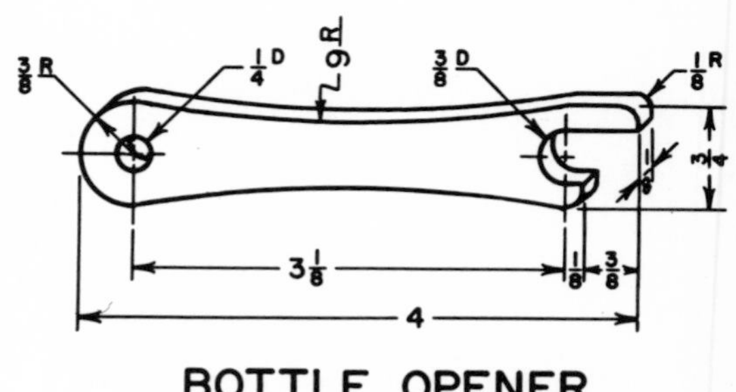

BOTTLE OPENER

1/4 D

$3\frac{1}{4}$

$4\frac{1}{2}$

1/16 THICK

OIL GASKET

Additional drawing problems--multiview.

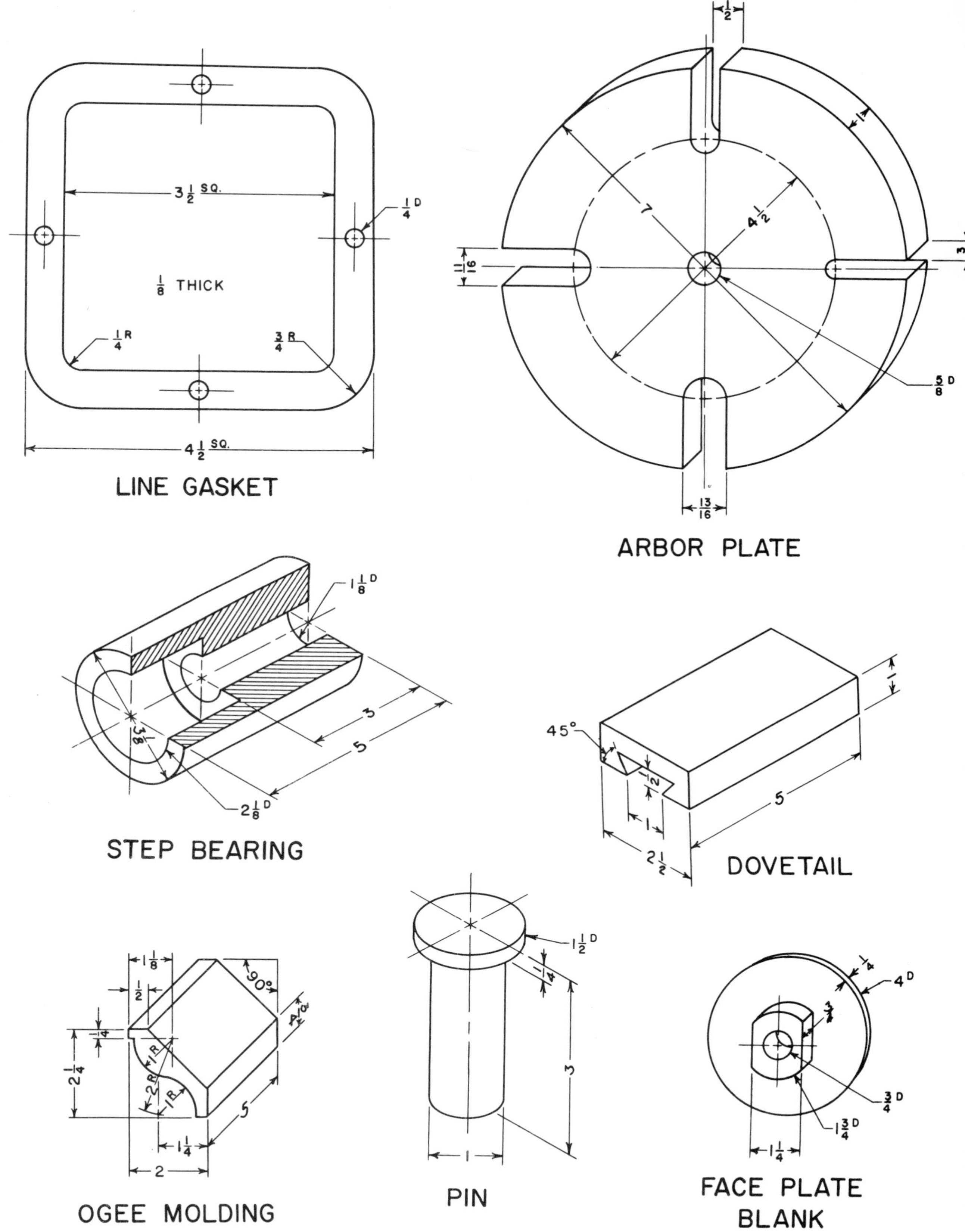

Additional drawing problems--multiview.

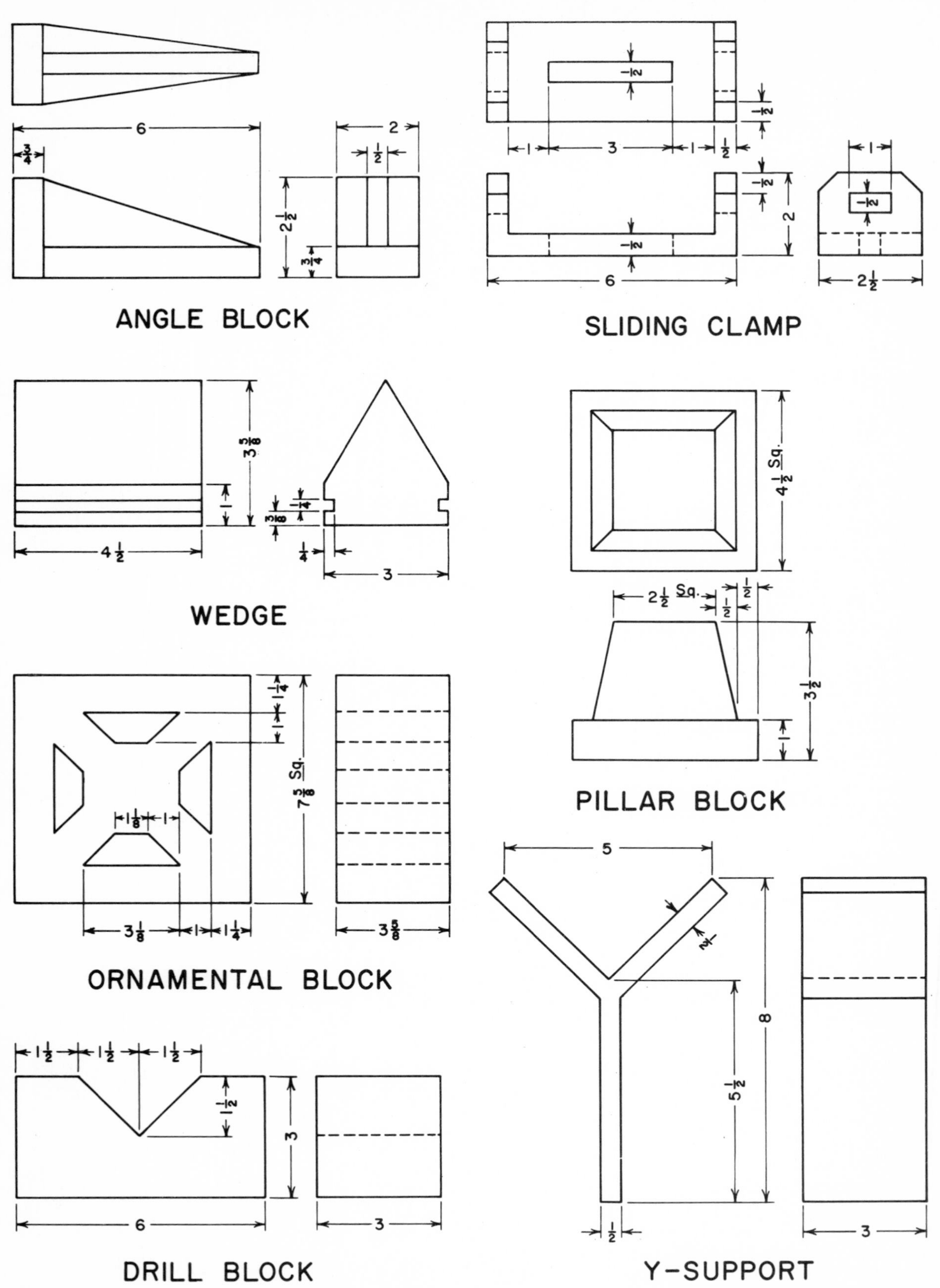

Additional drawing problems--pictorial.

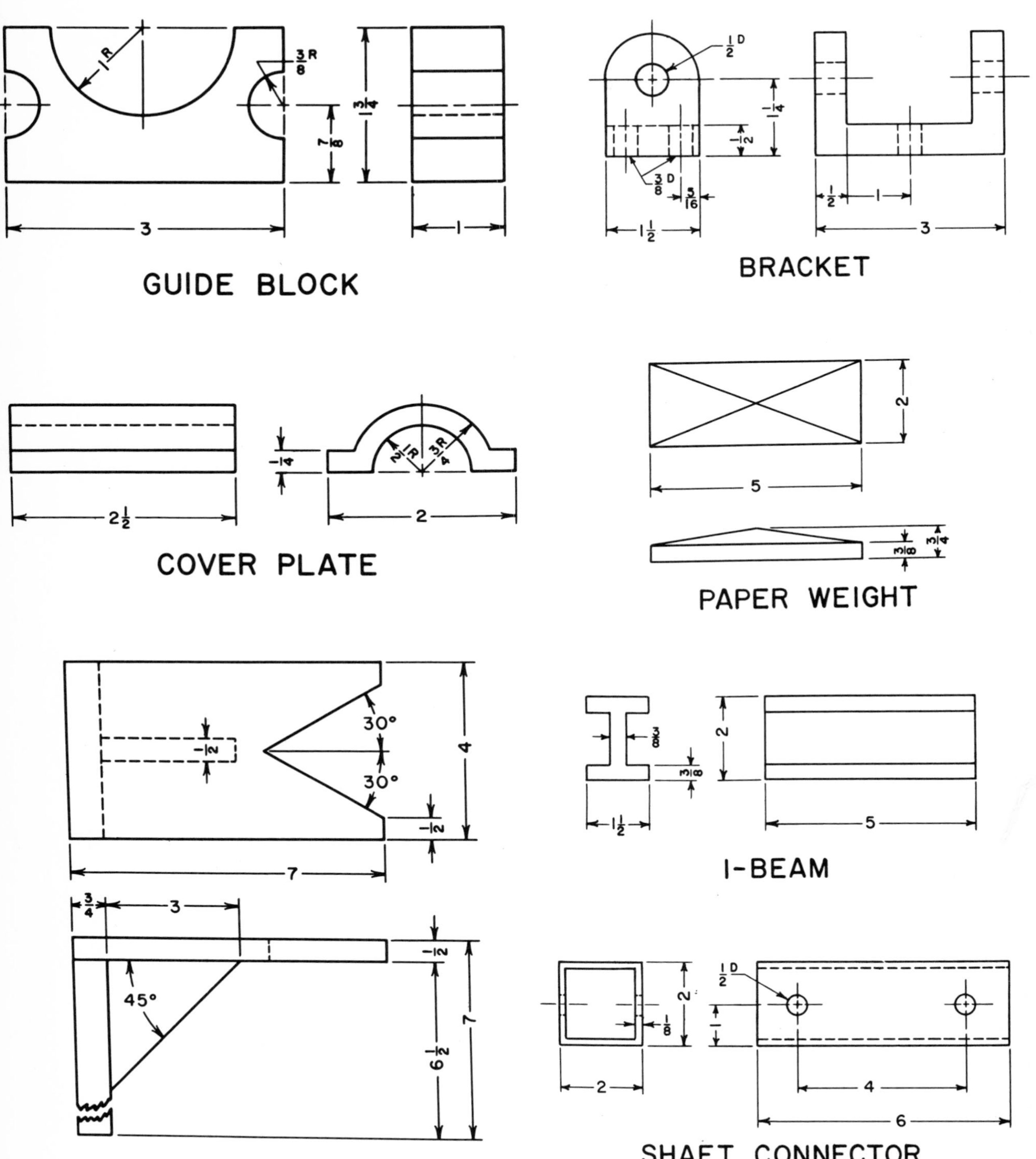

Additional drawing problems--pictorial.

INDEX